D1615337

ONCE UPON A VILLAGE

ONCE UPON
A VILLAGE
Sybil Marshall

Drawings by Ewart Oakeshott

J. M. DENT & SONS LTD
LONDON   MELBOURNE   TORONTO

First published 1979

© Sybil Marshall 1979

Printed in Great Britain by Billing & Sons Limited,
Guildford, London and Worcester.
for J. M. DENT & SONS LTD
Aldine House   Welbeck Street   London

This book is set in V.I.P. 11pt Bembo
by D.P. Media Limited, Hitchin, Hertfordshire

British Library Cataloguing in Publication Data

Marshall, Sybil
    Once upon a village.
    1. England – Social life and customs
    – 20th century
    2. Villages – England
    I. Title
    942.083'092'4   DA566.4

    ISBN 0-460-04435-4

Contents

For Claire and Cecil Chapman,
friends in deed

1 It takes all sorts . . .

Between two and four o'clock on Saturday afternoon, time stood still. Not just time by the clock on every mantelpiece, or the church clock that was always a few minutes slow; but Time, that looped yesterday together with tomorrow, and treated each today as insignificant, a tiny sliver of daylight to be tossed back at nightfall into the vast pool of eternity.

The late September sun had caught the village in a bowl of amber light, and stilled it there. At the bottom of the bowl lay its heart, where church, pub, village shop and school flanked the crossroads, in their various ways chronicling time past. The south and west faces of the broad, squat tower of the church glowed pink with sunshine absorbed by the stone in six hundred years of such Saturdays, while the north and east frowned darkly in blue-grey shadow. The shop, facing the church, was no more than the converted outshoot of a lath-and-plaster cottage with whitewashed walls and soft, dove-coloured thatch, its doors barely wide enough to admit the waddling bulk of old Martha when she came to collect her pension, or tall enough to accommodate the six-foot-four of the Professor when he came to buy peppermints, bent though his lean frame was with seventy years of gazing unseeing at the ground beneath his feet. The tiny gate opened on to a broken brick path (up which the entire village now tramped, tripped, shuffled or danced according to age and sex) that had been there when Elizabeth Tudor sat on the throne.

The school, on the other hand, bore witness to the puritan zeal of the worthies of Victoria's reign, having begun as a British School in 1864. Its dirty yellowish-grey brick and its uncompromising utility of design proclaimed it as a no-nonsense building, erected on the shoestring funds of public subscription, mainly nonconformist in origin. But therein lay its pride and its potency, for it owed nothing to the church either in its beginnings or now. In this respect, the village had always been able to cock a snook at its neighbours, all of which had schools still bearing the legend 'C. of E.' on their doors. This one had been taken over long ago by the local education authority, which kept it in repair, and decorated it—if dark green paint outside and a mixture of chocolate woodwork and bare whitewashed brick inside could be called decoration. Yet even here the golden afternoon was doing its best to be kind, lighting up the row of red bricks that ran round the walls at shoulder height, and catching the slates here and there with reflected sheen.

The inn, which stood well back from the road, was a miscellany of architecture. Only a narrow path separated it from the church, for that arm of the crossroads led nowhere except to Stavesacre Farm, beyond that imposing Queen Anne residence turning into a bridle path across fields to the next village. The path between church and inn was still only a cart-track wide, and curved out of sight as soon as it left the supporting rectitude of the churchyard wall, no doubt because the feet that marked it out in the first place were no steadier when they left The Star six hundred years ago than are feet today.

The abbots and priors of medieval times were a worldly-wise lot, in spite of their cowls. They knew the value of a bellyful of good English ale to the masons building their new churches, and saw to it that they didn't have far to go when

8

thirst overcame them at their labours. The part of The Star nearest to the church was contemporary with it, a long low room of lath and plaster, held together with solid oak beams inside and out. Its roof sagged under the weight of ancient tiles, and the great hearth filling almost all the end wall bulged inwards and outwards to accommodate a brick oven. A cool room this, in summer, with a slightly stand-offish air, as being too full of its own age and dignity to care much for today's fleeting occupants. It was not used much by the village, who preferred the tap and the bar parlour, the latter a reluctant concession to the few visitors who came in cars to visit the church, and to have a drink safely separated from the local inhabitants. Both these rooms were housed in the two-storeyed Tudor structure of red brick interlaced with timber that formed the middle part of the inn, and bore the sign of a single star creaking outside the front door.

The publican's private quarters, at the far end from the church, had been added in coaching days, and were vaguely eighteenth century in character, the tall windows contrasting strangely with their small Tudor neighbours in the middle and the even tinier peepholes in 'The Room', as the medieval section was called. In coaching days too, or at least in the heyday of horse transport, the stables had been built, one block at each end of the house, standing at right angles to it and thereby enclosing on three sides a cobbled yard, in the middle of which now stood a ring of ageworn benches, backing on to an ancient pump. Overshadowing it all from the back was a splendid walnut tree, laden with walnuts ready for picking. The stables were no longer needed for putting up horses or traps, let alone the carriages for which they had been built in the first place. One of the large airy barns contained the landlord's secondhand car. The others, on both sides, were stuffed full of bits and pieces he always intended to sort out and sell, but never did. On the side farthest away from the church, the end of the row of stables had been converted to a workshop for the landlord's bachelor brother Don, who was a cobbler by trade, but also obliged his mates in the village by cutting their hair or trimming their corns, according to which end needed the most urgent attention. He worked at his last by an ever-open door, even in midwinter, and the 'display' slab inside a modern plate-glass window was piled high with unclaimed boots and shoes, oddments of leather, nails and studs, tools and labels, and the fading wrappers of lines he had been tempted to try to sell years ago, and had completely forgotten.

When the weather was warm, the benches outside The Star were the natural meeting place of the old men who needed to sit down, and Don's shop the nucleus of those who could still stand. In inclement weather, the whole lot congregated round Don, who led the talk from a mouth full of nails and punctuated it with delicate taps of his hammer. The women used the benches too, on occasions when for any reason the shop was out of commission, or too full. Not that they patronized the landlord or his wares. Women, even those from the town eight miles away, or those passing through, were rare visitors to the pub as a place of refreshment. The redheaded bad lot of the village, who happened to be a pianist so gifted by nature that she could play anything and everything by ear as soon as she heard it, had long ago laid claim to the only piano in the village available to her, and that stood in the bar parlour of The Star. She was accepted by the men more as a bit of Charlie's bric-à-brac than as a woman. Ginger Margie entertained the company on most Saturday nights, to their delight and much reproving tongue-clicking by their wives, who watched the clock anxiously and counted every minute after closing time. The risk they thought they saw had been lessened of late, though, since the late-night bus from town had been re-routed to a point within walking distance of the village. Margie had found her various talents more appreciated in town, and The Star only saw her now on odd occasions during the week.

From this centre of operations, the village straggled up gentle slopes in three directions from the signpost that stood on the corner of the green, outside the school fence. There were cottages of two rooms only, some bungalows, some of the one-up-and-one-down variety; there were houses, very old and very beautiful, converted out of rows of cottages built in the middle ages. There were farmhouses, gracious and spacious, ranging from Tudor to Victorian, and there were modern brick-built bungalows, and a row of twelve pebble-dashed, semi-detached council houses, mercifully hidden from the centre of the village by a row of trees. The tiny Victorian schoolhouse, attached to the school, struck a mid-Victorian note of its own, and so did the Chapel, built in 1870 and still retaining a newish look of unqualified respectability, like a Salvation Army lass in uniform among a group of leisurely haymakers.

The rim of the shallow bowl in which the village lay was rounded with gently rising fields dappled everywhere with trees at present casting slightly lengthened shadows on the stubble. The fields gleamed silvery-white as the sun caught the curves left by the self-binders, for the summer had been hot, and the straw was dry and brittle to the touch. Here and there a field still remained to be carted, and stooks stood in immaculate rows, texturing the gold setting of the clearcut village cameo with triangular patterns of dark and light. Nothing stirred. The children, up early and already worn out with play, had drifted homewards towards Saturday's tea, which was always something a bit different from the usual weekday run of bread and jam. They were now sitting waiting listlessly in doorways or back gardens, crazing their mothers with their everlasting questions of 'What can I do'? Mum, what can I do?' Their mothers mostly ignored them, being occupied with other matters concerning tea soon to come, or their husband's clean shirt having lost an essential button just at the crucial point of change on Saturday afternoon. The men, with few exceptions, were in the process of their weekly ablutions, some in their newfangled bathrooms, but most over the kitchen sink. The shop was empty, all weekend shopping having been completed in the morning for such things as the shop supplied,

11

which was everything from homecured ham to cornplasters. Its goods were supplemented by bus trips to the market town, and by the mobile grocery that would not reach the village till nine or ten o'clock at night. Tom Swallow, who gave the village this extra service, did not expect much in the way of grocery trade at that late hour, but he was always sure of some because he was the only butcher who came within five miles of the village. Most people kept back an order for a few small items of grocery to encourage him to keep up his delivery of meat to them. He understood the system perfectly, and over-charged them for their Sunday joints just enough to make his long hours on the van worthwhile.

May Quinton still sat in the shop, behind the post-office grille at one side of the counter. The next time the village came to life again would be the intrusion of the mail van to collect the letters at around three-forty-five. She would have the kettle on in the back place, to give him his usual cup of tea and hear all the latest news of the other seven or eight villages he called at. Meanwhile, she took the opportunity of keeping up to date with her letters, minutes, agenda and the rest concerning the Women's Institute, of which she was the secretary. The door between the shop and the back room stood ajar, as it always did, and in the doorway the oversized chair containing the bulk of her oversized aunt practically blocked the way. The old lady was fast asleep, snoring occasionally, and puffing out her lips each time she exhaled. Now and again she raised her head and said, 'What did you say? I heard you. I ain't asleep,' before letting out the next gentle snore. The chapel and the chapelhouse, the schoolhouse and school, were still and quiet as the graves in the graveyard, patiently awaiting return to life on Sunday in the one case, and Monday in the other.

The Star was closed for the brief respite of time that Charlie and Dolly could call their own. She had gone upstairs 'for a bit of a lay down'. Charlie had announced his intention of polishing a few bits of brass in the shed, but was in fact fast asleep in

12

one of the many antique armchairs that cluttered up the place, his glasses on his forehead and a glass of light ale steadily losing its strength on a dusty though highly polished mahogany occasional table at his elbow.

A book lay open on his knees—a small, well-thumbed volume that he had picked up in a sale years ago. *Highwaymen and Robbers* ran the title. It had given Charlie hours of pleasure, for there were aspects of his rotund personality that were, so to speak, kept privy. He kept the pub to supplement the meagre pension his grateful country had awarded him for the hole in his back that was the result of a wound he got from a shell splinter at Jutland.

He had adored life in the navy, and was proud of having been a speck of dust adhering to the broad canvas of history. History was his secret passion, and antiques of all kinds seemed to him to be the nearest he could come to reliving homely bits of it. He bought odd lots at local auction sales, always intending to throw away the rubbish and 'turn a pretty penny' on the good stuff. He never did either. He was too occupied to bother about the junk, and it simply overflowed from one stable-barn into the next. The stuff that was good he fell in love with, and could not be persuaded to part with it for love nor money, as the saying goes. The public rooms accommodated as much of it as he could stuff in. The barn he called his den accommodated the rest. Dolly, his wife, had never understood his delight in it, or its value, but she had long since given up bothering her head about it. Her attitude towards his books was very different. She couldn't see what a man like him wanted with books and waged eternal warfare against print in any form, as she might have done against a more flesh and blood rival for her husband's time and attention. He was therefore driven to reading secretly, especially anything as far from Dolly's mental reach as history.

Charlie was a romantic at heart, and could people his private world with imaginary characters and events. As he polished a table picked up at a sale, he found himself wondering what

other hands had done the same in years gone by, and what
family quarrels had taken place round it. He never opened the
door of the particular barn he was now sitting in without half-
expecting a masked highwayman to rise from the shadows
and confront him with a pair of long-barrelled pistols. In
'the room' he felt, rather than imagined, time past and people
vanished. When he had taken over the pub from his father, he
had also taken over the furniture. It had probably been like that
for hundreds of years from one landlord to the next. Under the
window was a four-legged bench of dark oak, polished now
by many hands and countless bottoms, for when the room was
used it was a favourite seat. Few except Charlie recognized
it for what it was, a medieval coffin stool. If fascinated the
landlord with its macabre history, especially since he had once
happened to go into the church when the late Vicar had been
showing the Professor the precious church silver, and the
priceless registers as old as any in the country, the parson had
said. The Vicar had read aloud an entry, chosen at random.

*'BURYED THIS DAYE, THOMAS, SON OF
DICCON, AGED THREE YEARES, GOING TO
PLAYE IN YE BARNE, DID THERE FALLE INTO
A VAT OF HIS MOTHER'S HOME BREWED, AND
PERYSSHED.*
PRICE OF YE ALE, 4D.
IT WAS YE BESTE OCTOBER ALE.'

Charlie had no doubts at all that little Tom had skipped to
his death from the back door of 'the room', and that his tiny
rough coffin had rested on the coffin stool under the window
before being carried across to the newly consecrated
churchyard.

From the road to the graveyard, it was necessary to climb
three steep steps to reach the gate. A close look at the sur-
rounding wall, under the lichen and the ivy, revealed the
height at which new stones had been added years ago. The
difference in level from the road to the path that led from

the gate to the west door was now at least four feet, probably more. Little Tom was perhaps one of the first to lie there, but the rising level of this half-acre of land bore witness to the fact that he did not now lack company. In the end, one after another, the villagers had entered the churchyard on the shoulders of their stalwart neighbours, and had not come out again. Apart from the single funerals that had punctuated the years, there had been the Black Death, and the Great Plague, and the cholera outbreak in the nineteenth century, and the influenza epidemic of 1918. There was now no room for fresh graves, and had not been for many a year. When Whippet Tuck, old Martha's well-set son, dug a new grave, he was inured to turning up all sorts of grisly relics of the past, though he had made bitter complaint to the Vicar on one occasion recently when he'd turned up the coffin plate of the farmer his father used to work for. That, he felt, was a bit more than decent.

'It's them chapel lot,' he had grumbled. 'Ought to 'eve a graveyard o' their own. Never come near the church only ter git married an' buried.'

That was true, of course. Whippet was a loyal son of the church, and saw to it that all the chapel backsliders were put away on the north, dark side of the churchyard, where the sun rarely shone. The sunny side was reserved for his fellow communicants, and Whippet calculated their respective sanctity to a nicety before fetching out his probe to recommend a suitable place for the disposal of their remains. Those he approved of went closer to the church than those he didn't care a lot for. In this, he had his own way completely, because with the churchyard stuffed to overflowing as it was, neither vicar nor churchwardens dared gainsay him. Gravediggers were few and far between.

He had buried Old Watson right under the church wall, a year or two back. The Vicar had protested mildly on that occasion, saying it was the spot reserved, by age-old custom, for the incumbents of the parish when at last they joined their flock. Whippet had stood his ground, and won the day. He

15

had his plans for the future like everybody else. Old Watson had been very respected in his lifetime, the people's warden, too, for many a year. He was well over eighty when he departed. His wife, on the other hand, was still under seventy, and Whippet did not approve of her, church organist though she might be. He had put old Watson in as close to the church wall as he could manage, and was reserving a spot just inside the gate for the widow. Whippet had a nicely balanced sense of justice, and felt that anybody who had endured that nimble tongue for more than fifty years deserved his respite.

Mrs Watson was one of the four women in the church that sleepy September afternoon. The air inside the ancient building was cool and fresh and scented with the many indefinable smells of age. The flags underfoot were spotless, the chancel carpet leading to the altar without a speck of dust. The sun was still catching the stained glass on the south side, and flung brilliant patches of red and blue at random on the floor, making it a sanctuary of light and colour.

Mrs Watson had hastily jammed a few Michaelmas daisies and a bit of golden rod into the vases on the altar, because tomorrow was only the lay-reader's day to take Evensong in the afternoon. She had no time for the pompous lay-reader, a small bearded teacher from The School. Not the village school, of course, but *the* school, the public school that occupied The Priory, a seventeenth-century mansion that had incorporated the ruins of the medieval priory when it had been built for the first duke. Now it was a boarding school, to which only very few local boys ever attained. The Duke himself lived in The Lodge, when in residence, from where he kept a tolerant eye on the school, and a far less tolerant one on his tenant farmers.

Once a month, the church had Morning Prayer at 11 am and Evensong at 6 pm, and claimed the services of the Vicar for most of the day. He had a bigger church and parish three miles away, and still another two miles off in the other direction, to care for. On Sundays, he officiated hurriedly at Communion at 8 am, and on every alternate one came back for Evensong in the afternoon. One Sunday each month, it fell to the lay-reader Monty Price, one of the masters at the Priory School, to conduct Evensong. His role on the fourth Sunday was that of choirleader, for on that Sunday the whole Priory School was expected to attend morning service, and its excellent choir led the singing, while another master played the organ. Strange to say, Mrs Watson had never resented this intrusion on her rights. It gave her a chance, once a month, to review the worshippers from a different angle, and to update her speculations about them. She had to agree that Mr Proud could make the organ nearly talk; but she believed honestly, if complacently, that her own fumblings on the keys were more suited to the queer medley of voices, mostly female, that she generally accompanied.

She was now pretending to sort out her music for tomorrow, though in effect the lay-reader had not so far favoured her with his choice of hymns. This had happened several times just lately. Where did he go on Saturday afternoons? Usually he took a walk to the village after morning lessons, posted some letters, and dropped the list of hymns through the door of 'Heatherleigh'. May Quinton said the letters were always to his old mother, a friend in a similar school in Durham, and occasionally to his bank manager. But for the last few weeks, he had posted no letters through the village postbox, and the list of hymns had been handed to Mrs Watson on Sunday mornings just before service. There was mystery there. It must be looked into.

Of the three other women in the church, two were polishing brass candlesticks on the vestry table. One was the spinster schoolmistress's dependent spinster sister. She had been delicate as a child, and still looked it, which made a good excuse for her domineering headmistress sister to keep her at home as an unpaid housekeeper. Miss Nellie, as she was universally called, had just enough of a pittance from an older brother who had gone to foreign parts and died unmarried there to supply

17

her other wants. There was about Miss Nellie, however, a frail strength of character, and an occasional twinkle in her hazel eyes that prevented anybody from adding the adjective 'poor' before her cognomen, as they did naturally about 'poor Alice', who played the wheezy chapel organ on alternate weeks.

With Miss Nellie was a gaunt lean woman, whose tall frame and air of dark intensity highlighted Nellie's frail, faded fairness. Elsie Winters was still on the right side of fifty, and handsome in a forbidding sort of way. Her outstanding feature was the long bony jaw, one that might have served Samson well if he had happened to come on it at Ramathlehi, instead of that of the ass with which he slew his thousand. Above the equally bony nose burned a pair of black eyes in deep hollow sockets. She polished the candlestick in her hand with a sort of sadistic thoroughness, as though it were the world she was cleansing of its manifold sins and wickednesses. There was no mistake about Elsie Winters. What she did, she made a good job of, even if it took her, as she would have said, 'forever and a day'. She was the wife of Perce Winters, who was horsekeeper up at Cudweed Farm. Since Jack Marriatt had lost his wife a couple of years ago, Elsie had added the care of him and his rambling farmhouse to that of her own home and family. 'If you want anything doing, go to a busy person,' she would say, and it was usually good advice. Jack Marriatt had been people's warden at church after Old Watson had given it up, and his wife had always cleaned the brasses every Saturday. He had only half-suggested to Elsie that she might add this also to her list of responsibilities, but she had leapt at it, quoting her favourite maxim, and adding, 'While you're busy, you ain't got time for scandal, that's what I always say. Busy hands stop idle tongues. I don't like scandal. That's why I've got the time to do things as other women haven't.'

She was talking now to Miss Nellie. Mrs Watson could hear their voices rising and falling, but guessed there wasn't much to interest her going on between them. Mrs Jeffs, now, the woman dusting pews and putting out hymnbooks, was a different cup of tea. She had been but nine years in the village, and had only very recently been accepted by the indigenous population, though she had married a native. The thing was that she was still a bit of a mystery. She was always ready for a talk, and very interesting her tales were, for she had been round the world several times, apparently, with her first husband. She was an educated woman, too, and that made it all the queerer that she had married old Tom Jeffs, who, to use his wife's expression, had 'snuffed it' last year, leaving her with one child of her own, eight of his, and three of theirs. Mrs Watson had no doubt that she would worm out the story of that ill-assorted match sooner or later.

In the meantime, Mrs Jeffs often knew in good time what was happening in the farm stratum of village life. She was vice-president of the Women's Institute this year, and a couple of farmer's wives also did their bit at the WI's monthly meetings. Mrs Watson had no use for the WI. 'I belong to the Mother's Union,' she had said primly, when asked to join. With those words, she had cleaved the female population of the village into two groups. It had been tacitly accepted thereafter that if you had previously belonged to the long-established MU, you must *ipso facto* be against an upstart rival organization like the WI. This was the one area in which church and chapel were not on opposite sides. Before May Quinton's advent to take over the village post office and look after her aged aunt, there had been no WI. Church and chapel women alike had joined the society dedicated to the upholding of Christian marriage—at least, those that had time to spare had done so. They met once a month in the home of the Enrolling Member, who was the widow of a minor canon. They trailed along to her house in ones and twos, carrying prayer books in one hand and a plate of buns in the other. As May Quinton observed wickedly to Mrs Jeffs, there was only one mother amongst them, other than the Enrolling Member herself. Five unmarried ladies of uncertain age, seven childless widows, and two wives who so far had not produced babies, though rumour had it that they were trying hard, in one case with the help of an Irish lodger. Mrs Watson was one of the childless widows.

She watched as Mrs Jeffs finished dusting the last pew, and drifted towards the vestry. Then she joined them. Elsie was nearly striking sparks from the brass in her hands with the vigour of her polishing.

'I never did like it, an' I never shall,' she was saying. 'It seems to me as if you ask for it, you're bound to get it. I reckon Old Nick waits for 'em, with his pitchfork in his hand. "All right," he says, " 'Ell fire you've asked for, and 'ell fire you shall 'ev!" and pushes the coffin into the flames hisself! You'll never get me to believe as any o' The Family will be cremated. There's plenty o' room in the family vault still, ain't there?'

'Well,' said Miss Nellie mildly, 'I was only telling you what my sister had heard.'

'Hearsay!' snapped Elsie. 'I don't go on hearsay. It never can be said as I talk scandal.' The candlestick received its ultimate polish, and she clapped it down smartly beside its fellow, and prepared to fold up her cloths.

'What's all this then?' asked Mrs Watson, moving in to stand by Miss Nellie's side in the place Elsie had vacated. 'Who's going to be cremated?'

Mrs Jeffs sat down, pulling up the one chair the vestry contained.

'I think it's a lot more healthy than burying folks,' she said. 'If you'd seen the corpses floating in the river, in India, like I have, it'd make you think again about such things.' She settled herself comfortably, ready to give them the benefit of her travelled erudition, for she always found Miss Nellie a good listener. But Mrs Watson had scented news of a much more immediate nature, and was not going to be put off the trail by corpses in the Ganges. She ignored Mrs Jeffs and said again directly to Miss Nellie: 'Who's going to be cremated, then?'

'Nobody that I know of, yet,' said Miss Nellie. 'I only happened to mention to Mrs Winters that my sister went up to the school for coffee with the housemaster of Gibbon, to talk about Roland Pettigrew's work. They're very pleased with him, holding his own in his form, so they say, though nearly all the others are from private schools and prep. schools. My sister's very proud of him.

'While she was there, it happened to come up about what Roly had written in an essay he'd been set, something about the way folks used to cremate people in olden days, and put their bones into urns, or something. Roly had put in his essay that nobody was going to do that him, 'cos he was going to be hung. And they'd all laughed about it. Then the housemaster's wife had said there'd come a time when everybody would have to be cremated by law; and her husband had said they wouldn't need a law, if a few people like the Duke got themselves done, because it would set the fashion. And he said he had heard the Duke did favour cremation. That's all.'

There was food for a lot of good future gossip wrapped up in Miss Nellie's report. For the moment, the juxtaposition of the living Duke and the disposal of his aristocratic remains was too juicy a morsel to swallow without a good chew.

Mrs Watson fiddled with her cotton gloves, and wished for a slightly less critical and genteel audience; but she could not resist the urge to say what had risen to her tongue.

'Well, he might as well go straight to hellfire of his own accord as not, and I daresay he knows it,' she said. 'He's got plenty to answer for, I'll be bound!' She snorted with righteous knowledge, and leaned forward to continue *sotto voce* if invited by word or look.

Elsie Winters buttoned up her coat. 'If you are going to run down The Family, I'll be going,' she said. 'I don't talk scandal, and I don't listen to it. I'll bid you good-day.' She went, her chin thrust forward to lead the way. Miss Nellie reluctantly followed. She didn't often get the pleasure of tasty gossip, because people in general respected her forty-year-old virginity, and had a healthy awe of her sister's schoolmarmish authority. When she too had gone, the other ill-assorted couple were left in the calm, cool, clean atmosphere of the hallowed building.

Mrs Watson, taking the plunge, said as an opening gambit: 'I wonder if he'll leave Margie anything in his will!'

Mrs Jeffs' jaw dropped in spite of herself. That was unexpected. 'Margie?' she said. 'Do you mean to say that old man——' but she got no further.

'Of course, you couldn't be expected to know, 'cos Margie must be eighteen or nineteen now, and you ain't been here all that long, after all—though your Tom must have known about it. Funny if he didn't tell you.'

'We had other things to do,' said Mrs Jeffs unwisely.

'Ah. No doubt,' said Mrs Watson, somehow managing to convey in three words a picture of Tom and his two wives, surrounded by twelve kneeling progeny (as in the Tudor memorial to a former village worthy at the other end of the church). 'No, not Margie! But she ain't got that red hair for nothing!' Now as the present duke was as bald as a coot, Mrs Jeffs did not quite understand the innuendo, though she gathered that there was one.

'Red hair?' she prompted.

'All The Family have got red curly hair when they're young. The men lose it early—but you should see the women. I've seen a good many that belong to 'em. Margie's the spit image.'

'Is she some relation to The Family, then?' Mrs Jeffs had a consuming interest in the upper ten. Had she not once entertained the Prince of Wales to lunch on her first husband's rancho in Brazil?

Mrs Watson swung her cotton gloves from side to side, gazing upward in delight at Mrs Jeffs' obvious ignorance. 'Some relation? Dearie me O! Some relation!'

Mrs Jeffs tried hard to put two and two together. Margie's mother was as stolid, careworn, unattractive a female as the village held, much married, and with five other children besides Margie, all of whom had hair that varied from true auburn to carroty red. The mind boggled.

'But her mother's red-haired,' protested the doubting newcomer.

'That's as maybe. It's one thing to think, and another to know, as my old father used to say. Only he used to say it in his own way. "Knowing beats thinking's arse off," he'd say, and he was right. How do I know? 'Cos George Willis told me. He had to go out one night late to a cow as started calving out in a field. He'd took a storm lantern with him to look for the cow in the dark. Nearly fell over 'em, so he said. Well, what he did say was that he see 'em in the ditch under the hedge, busy as bees—you know George! "Busy as a couple o' bloody bees," he said—only I don't like to swear, specially in here. But that's what he told me, out of his own mouth.'

It was time to go, and both women knew it. Mrs Jeffs felt some sort of reply was expected.

'I can't believe it, whatever George Willis said,' she answered. 'After all, a duke! He could have his pick anywhere, I should think. Doesn't seem right for him to be under a hedge with a plain Jane like that!'

'There's them as like it that way for a change, no doubt. Dearie me O! I could tell you a few things about others, that I could.'

She took a last proprietary look round the cool, clean, colour-filled church. Her glance rested for a moment on the hammerbeam roof, swept up the nave by the sturdy columns and followed the strip of blue carpet to the altar, where her hastily arranged flowers had been reunited with the burnished candlesticks on 'the fair linen'. Lastly, it lingered for a moment on the Wytton memorial. That, her nod intimated, upheld her argument better than words.

'A hungry dog'll gnaw any old bone,' she said with finality. The sideways look she gave to The Family vault as she edged by it to the little side gate seemed to suggest some apprehension on her part with regard to the dead ducal dogs, even in broad daylight. By bedtime, the whole village was either burying or burning the Duke, according to individual fancy, though His Grace had in fact spent a happy day plodding through Scottish heather with a tweed pork pie protecting his baldness, and a gun in the crook of his arm, very much alive. Mrs Jeffs had to call on May Quinton, on WI business. She found Bob the postman sitting astride a wooden chair, balancing a cup and saucer on the back of it. May was serving Mrs Bluett at the shop counter. Mrs Bluett trotted down to the shop on most days. Her custom rarely warranted May's effort to get by her enormous aunt, but her presence was always welcome, all the same. Mrs Bluett brightened the day for May, leaving behind her as she almost always did an addition to the list of her extraordinary liberties with the language. May enjoyed Mrs Bluett, though she rarely had anyone to share the gems with.

May had her fair share of trials. She had been brought up by two aunts, who had lived all their lives in the house where May now sat. Late in life, one of them had married a cabinet-maker, and the strain had been too much for her. When she had been buried in a lavish coffin made by her husband, he had lived on with his sister-in-law, and May. She had been a bright girl, and had won a free place to the grammar school, but at sixteen she had left school and gone to London—run away, in fact.

When the surviving aunt had decided to become an invalid, May had been sent for, and the breach healed. She came, bringing with her two children, but no husband. He was, it appeared, in the navy, and stationed in some outlandish, unpronounceable 'foreign part'. All the children knew was the name of his ship, the *Warspite*. Nothing more was to be got from them.

The village accepted May's return with the minimum of comment. She had been born there. Besides, she was on to a good thing, because Aunt Mabel and Uncle Bert were both believed to be 'very warm' with this world's goods.

May's time in London had polished her rural education with a quick-witted urban gloss. She needed constant occupation and mental stimulus to counter Uncle Bert's politics and Aunt Mabel's domineering, carping criticism. When approached as prospective secretary for the newly formed WI, she was delighted, and officiated with cool efficiency, as she did behind the post office side of the counter. But she was often bored, and viewed the inhabitants of her native village with an objectivity few others were capable of. Some of them made her impatient, but mostly it was a tolerance born of understanding that made her such as asset to them. Her customer now had her whole attention, while Bob sipped his tea in leisurely fashion, and Aunt Mabel fiddled with her hearing aid. Nobody's business was hidden from Aunt Mabel.

Mrs B. stood at the counter, a small, bent, bedraggled figure in a shapeless black overcoat, despite the heat. May remarked to Aunt Mabel afterwards that she had never seen Mrs B. without a coat—without that coat, to be precise. It was always buttoned on one button over a pinafore that hid all other garments except the roll collar of a dusty-black jumper. Grey lisle stockings wrinkled round skinny legs protruded beneath the undulating hem of the coat, ending in a pair of low shoes buttoned across the instep, the kind parlourmaids wore as house shoes. Not that Liza Bluett's general appearance was of any real significance—no more than the husk that conceals a juicy kernel, or more than a coffin-likeness concealing the cocooned mummy many layers inside. It was simply not possible to conceive of Mrs Bluett as anything but a talking face, with a mouth pouring out torrents of sound that mesmerized her hearers like the eye of the Ancient Mariner, whose soul-sister she must surely be.

Her face, surrounded by a mop of unruly iron-grey hair bobbed at home with a pair of blunt scissors and held on each temple by a pink celluloid slide, seemed to be made of gutta-percha that could be pulled into all shapes at will. As Roddy Pettigrew (the older brother of Roly and the village madcap wit) said, you kept expecting it to come off altogether and float away. The nose-tip and ear lobes moved up, down and from side to side when she spoke, pulled every which way by an extraordinary mouth. That orifice was as near square as it is possible for a human mouth to be, and when open revealed a set of utterly toothless gums as mobile as the rest of the physiognomy. Her eyes were bright and clear, even sparkling, when she had launched into a tale; but one was brown and the other blue, so that she managed to give the appearance of being two women talking at once, especially as her voice, cracked like a broken bell, was normally raised to stentorian pitch—the penalty of living as a child with a whole family of deaf brothers.

She was holding forth when Mrs Jeffs entered, bawling good-naturedly in extra loud tones in order to make Aunt Mabel hear. That lady ostentatiously tuned down her hearing-aid and shook her head from side to side like a dog coming out of a pond, to indicate that she was being deafened.

'Don't shout so, woman!' she said. 'I can hear you. I'm not deaf. Only a little hard of hearing.'

Mrs B's mouth became trapezoidal as she smiled in the middle of her harangue at the idiosyncrasies of the deaf, about which she knew plenty, without pausing in her story.

'Yes,' she yelled, 'three whole vans full of 'em, with horses at the back and dogs running at the side. Gippoes, my husband says, but I said no, diddikies. They ha'n't got the proper look o' gippoes, I said. Then one of 'em stops an' asks me if I can direct 'em to Stavesacre Farm. Well, I says, I ought to be able to, seein' as I were born there, in one o' the cottages at the back o' the farmhouse. Course they ain't habituated now, I says, them cottages. Mr Pettigrew said they weren't fit for human habitation, so we all moved into the council houses, and he only uses them now to keep phosphorescent of lime in.'

May nodded in a vain attempt to stop the flow long enough for her to take in the meaning.

Bob rose, and the bell tinkled as Mrs Jeffs shut the door

unnecessarily behind her. Mrs B's mouth remained squarely, toothlessly opened, waiting for a chance to continue.

'I shall have to be going, Mrs Quinton,' said Bob. 'Thanks for the tea. Gippoes down at Stavesacre, eh? That's something new, I must say.' He reached the door before dropping his own scrap of news into the pot, and giving it a practised stir.

'I expect you'll all be going to the wedding, shan't you?' He was gone, well aware of the dumbfounded silence of four speechless women behind him. Next minute, he opened the door again, to pick up the mailbag he had left, accidentally on purpose, hanging on the back of his chair.

May found her voice first. 'Wedding?' she said. 'Whose?'

'Ah, that'd be telling,' Bob said, 'but I heard it on my way here, that there's a wedding or two likely to be soon. See you Monday, Mrs Quinton.' He really had gone, this time. The women explored each other's faces for any glimpse of fore-knowledge, while each put in a suggestion.

'Margie? I did hear she's been courting the new mechanical man at the garage.'

'Roddy Pettigrew?' (Mrs Jeffs.)

'Emma Rolph?' (Aunt Mabel.) 'Or one of the teachers up at the school?'

They were flummoxed, and had to admit it. Mrs B. gathered her package up, and her change, and opened the door, anxious to get home now, in case any of her council-house neighbours had the answer to Bob's riddle. She left open the shop door, and reached the gate, pausing to latch it carefully, because this brought her round to face the shop door again. She held up a cheery hand to those inside, and let out a stentorian roar.

'Ah well! We shall see what transfers now.'

The village had suddenly come to life again, like a cat stretching every paw and whisker after a long nap. The sun was dropping a bit, and the light was even more amber than ever. The smell of frying pork sausages wafted across the street in more than one place, as children began to drift aimlessly about again, still licking their fingers. Dogs and cats came out of the warm shadows, and trotted purposefully off on business of their own. From Pellmell came the lowing of cows awaiting milking, and from Stavesacre the voice of the horsekeeper calling in his mares for suppering up, a little early because of its being Saturday. Another week had begun.

2 A place for everything . . .

It was the five farms and three smallholdings that held the social structure of the village together. To the uninitiated, there was little to distinguish Garlick Farm (George Willis's domain) from Pellmell, where the Woodward family still struggled along. There was little difference in acreage, and if anything the farmyard at Garlick was in better condition than the dilapidated ruins round the house at Pellmell. Yet Pellmell was a farm, and Garlick a smallholding. The distinction lay somewhere in the collective subconscious of the village.

The smallholders played a vital part in the social hierarchy, being at one and the same time the links and buffers between the farmers and the labourers, many of whom bore names that appeared again and again in the medieval parish records.

This hierarchy was akin to the Almighty, insofar as it was eternal and omnipotent. It had been there, apparently from the beginning, never deliberately created, but of its own nature continually creative. It imposed itself on the individuals, one generation after another. For the indigenous, it was there to be drawn into themselves with their newborn cries. What few newcomers there were soon accepted it, because it was too strong for their puny protests, if indeed they ever made any. The odd ones who did so soon found that the chain was wellnigh unbreakable. In face of danger or interference, the opposite ends of it linked together, forming a tight ring that locked the protester firmly out.

The tensile strength of the system lay in its fine gradations, so subtle as to be almost imperceptible, yet tacitly acknowledged and completely apprehended by all within it. It worked, mainly because everyone wanted it to work. The element common to every link in the chain was proper pride.

Nobody ever said, 'I know my place,' because it would have been ridiculous as well as demeaning to voice a sentiment so obvious. If anyone had done so, it would have been said to establish pride of place, not as a declaration of subservience. 'A place for everybody, and everybody in his place' created an unbroken chain of emotional security, whatever the material conditions happened to be.

There was comfort in the knowledge that there was someone equally stable at each side of you on the social ladder; someone higher up, yet not out of reach, to whom you could turn in doubt, danger or distress; and at the same time there was someone else a rung lower down, to boost your self-esteem by seeking the same kind of reassurance from you.

'You can always find somebody worse off than yourself' was a bit of philosophy based on experience. Even 'Appy 'Arry, the layabout old drunkard who had, even in his youth, barely worked hard enough to keep body and soul together, was a notch or two up on tramps, gipsies and diddikies.

At the top of the structure was the Duke, beyond whom the ladder disappeared into the realm of God and the angels. But 'Appy 'Arry and the Duke had a lot in common, and liked each other's company. 'Arry was seldom drunk when the Duke was in residence, especially if a shoot was in the offing. He had been beating for the Duke since they were boys together, in the time when 'Arry's expert poacher father had kept his family from going hungry by his art. 'Arry had learned all the tricks young, and it was the main reason why he never went hungry now.

A PLACE FOR EVERYTHING . . .

The Duke's gamekeepers swore and cursed him to the limit of their extensive vocabulary, but 'Arry's larder was rarely empty. Cursing was as far as they went. They had had their orders to look the other way when 'Arry was up to his tricks with brandy-soaked sultanas threaded on fine cotton in the pheasant preserves.

Within this strange, flexible but unchanging pattern, Jack was as good as his master, and both knew it. There was mutual dependence, and a measure of mutual respect in consequence.

Money talked, as it always does, but its vociferousness alone did not earn respect. Education of the kind that smacked of 'book learning' was awarded more deference, and accorded the same tolerant interest, the same suspended judgment, as might have been given to a new breed of pig or the latest bit of agricultural machinery. If Perce Winters felt any resentment at the thirty-two shillings and sixpence wage paid to him for a seven-day week by Jack Marriatt on Saturdays, it was not directed at Jack, whose own struggles to keep his head above water Perce witnessed at close quarters. If Perce complained—and being human, he often did—it was because he couldn't swallow the discrepancy between his own apparent worth in terms of £.s.d. and that of Miss Taylor who ran the school.

'They reckon she gets five hundred pound a year!' he said, bitterly and unbelievingly to Charlie, on one of his infrequent visits to The Star. (Elsie did not approve of pub company.)

'Well,' said Charlie, with cheerful philosophy designed to prevent argument by nipping it neatly in the bud, 'if she didn't have it, you wouldn't get it. So what the hell does it matter?'

Perce felt there ought to be an answer to that, but it was so manifestly true that he couldn't see round the edges of it.

'Don't seem right, though, to me,' he persisted. 'I mean, her bein' a woman an' all. Only works from nine to ha'past three, Monday to Friday, an' gets her money just the same when there ain't no school in the holidays. Ten pound a week for that! Don't seem right, somehow.'

31

'Appy 'Arry, spending his old-age pension in the chimney corner, viewed the matter from a different perspective, being a man who had made it a practice to get along all right without work.

'It a' depends!' he said. 'It a' depends! It a' depends 'ow you look at it. I reckon you've got a good job up at Cudweed, Perce. Would you give it up an' take her job over?'

'Well, I couldn't, could I?' said Perce, groping after irrefutable fact with which to floor 'Arry, while tacitly yielding to Charlie. (The System dictated the pattern.)

'That's different!' said 'Arry. 'I said "would you", not "could you". I know I wouldn't change places with her, not for nothink I wouldn't. Well, not unless they'd let me strangle a couple o' the little buggers whenever I felt like it. Child'en ought to be drownded like kittens, afore they get their eyes open. That's what I say.'

'But there, you will get 'em! You will get 'em! If the likes o' you 'ould lay still abed a-Sunday mornin's, there'd be no call for the likes of 'er.'

Perce, whose progeny amounted to no more than a modest brace, already grown up, was denied any crushing reply he might have made by the noise of the lifting of the latch, and Charlie's eloquent nod towards the door as Bert Stobbs came in. May Quinton's Uncle Bert was one of the few who had no part in The System. Though he had lived in the village for years and years, he was still 'a foreigner' from the town miles away. He had married Aunt Mabel's younger sister Clara after a very long and desultory courtship kept alive by the inevitability of a funeral in the village every now and then, for Bert's main occupation was the making of coffins. He still worked for the undertaker whose 'discreet funeral service' covered a wide area.

Bert's trouble was that he was a man with a grievance—an unalterable, unassuageable but unforgettable grievance.

At the age of twelve, he had been sent for by the headmaster of the school he and his horde of younger brothers attended.

The teacher had told him that he was the cleverest, most diligent and neatest-fingered pupil in the school, and that he had been highly recommended for one of the scholarships given annually at the local grammar school. Then he was sent home with the good news. His mother, looking up from her washtub, had merely replied, 'We shall 'ave to see what your dad says.' When his father came home, what he did say was unprintable. Then he followed it with a tirade about men such as the beeing headmaster, who wanted to take the bread out of the very mouths of Bert's brothers and their parents, expecting them to go on supporting lazy sons who were growed into men already.

'If you're so clever a'ready, you don't need no more of his sort o' learning! I'll thank him to mind his own business. I'll see you never set foot in his school no more, if I go to gaol for it. There's a coffin to be finished this afternoon. Get your jacket off. You'll help me to finish it and none of your lip. I'll scholarship you, that I will!'

So he had never been back to school again, and that evening had helped in awe and terror to fill the coffin he had watched his father shape and trim.

Many years later, when his father died and he was already the embittered breadwinner for the family, he asked his mother the reason for the strange second name that he bore. 'Albert Wimperris Stobbs' was written in a fine copperplate hand on all his belongings.

It was the old, old story, repeated in every generation up and down the land. His great-grandmother had been in service, and had come home in disgrace. The child she produced had needed no swearing as to parentage—the girl was pretty, and the earl had four strapping sons. She had been well compensated, however, and the boy had been given the name of the family as a first name.

Since then it had been a source of pride for the oldest son of each generation to be burdened with the reminder of his artistocratic connections.

Bert felt a singular pride in his lineage, and tried to live up to it in a dozen little ways that the village took against from the very first. But the knowledge of his ancestry added greatly to his railings against fate. The Earl of Wimperris was one of the greatest landowners in the country, with a pack of hounds famous all over the land. If, said Bert, all yuman beings were created equal in the sight of the Lord, as all yuman beings undoubtedly were, then marriage lines were only a manmade trick for doing such as himself out of their rightful dues. His grandfather had been the rightful heir (he said 'hair') to the Wimperris title and estates. But for this bit of yuman misman-agement, Bert Stobbs would now be the Earl of Wimperris.

The near miss had turned him into a radical, desirous of uprooting every legitimate privilege in others. The victory of Ramsay Macdonald's party had given his musings a local habitation and a name. He recognized himself as a Socialist. Now that he knew, he would serve under the red flag of Labour for ever.

There were many in the village who leaned in the same political direction, but their time had not yet come. In any case, they would never have allowed Bert the satisfaction of feeling their support, however feeble it might be. He 'roughed them up the wrong way' with his 'yuman beings' and his continual demands for his 'rightful dues'. Besides, he did not, and would not, acknowledge their Duke.

'I've got as good blood in me as he has,' he would aver, over and over again. 'Older than his is, my blood is,' he would say. 'His family are upstarts—by-blows from one of Charles the Second's 'ay-mures.'

The men of the village knew nothing about hay-mures, but were agreed that they didn't much like the sound of them, or care for Bert laying them at The Family's door. The Duke was a part of their pattern, whatever his origin. They could do very well without a crack-jawed coffin-maker. They tolerated him with dogged patience and mimicked him in private with heavy-footed sarcasm. They were often forced by their code

34

of politeness to listen to him, but they rarely talked to him or with him. His only real crony was the one communist the village contained, a tall, rugged, dour man who spoke to nobody but Bert, except to raise his voice at the parish meeting once a year.

The largest of the five farms was Campion's Hall. This was not an integral part of the village proper, because the elegant Georgian residence stood more than a mile distant, and could be reached from that direction only by cart-tracks through woods and fields. The house itself had access to a main road in a different direction. But the fields of Campion's Hall Farm lurked on the outskirts of the village, and abutted on to those of Stavesacre. They were conspicuous in their appearance of trim prosperity in a time of deep agricultural depression, always first to be ploughed in the autumn, first to be drilled, first to be harvested. Hedges and ditches were cut back and cleaned out; fences were whole and buildings weatherproof. Every year new machinery appeared on the farm, to be viewed askance, and barely commented on in The Star of a Saturday night. The men, from farmer to casual labourer, eyed it with distrust, if with unwilling admiration. What Campion seemed to demonstrate was the procreation of efficiency without love, and they didn't see how that was possible. The truth really was that the villagers had, in their age-old way, weighed its present owner in the balance, and found him wanting, though it would have puzzled anyone to say what it was that he lacked.

He was, of course, 'a gentleman farmer', and that was nearly enough by itself. Gentlemen (real gentle-men) could be farmers; and farmers could be, and often were, gentlemen. But the hybrid who called himself 'a gentleman farmer' scored on neither count.

Time was, as many in the village would gladly tell you, when Campion was a proper farm, and its owner, 'the old squire', a proper farmer, and a real 'cure'.

'You see, he were a bachelor as never had no truck with womenfolk,' Dick Rivers would say. 'My grandad were his groom, and they used to hunt whenever they got a chance. Ah—a beautiful lot of 'osses they had up there then I've 'eard tell. Out on a frosty morning they'd be for a meet somewhere, miles and miles away—there were no such thing in them days as sending your groom with the 'osses and following him by car when you were ready, like now. You hacked to the meet, and that meant a 'nation early start, many a time.

'My old grandad used to be up at four o'clock, them mornings, baiting his mares. Then 'e'd groom 'em till you could see your face in the shine on 'em, and he'd polish the tack till the sweat rolled off him. When he were ready, 'e'd saddle up, and take the 'osses round to the front o' the Hall just after seven o'clock, and there wouldn't half be a scene if he were a minute late, 'cos the Old Squire 'ould be standing in the porch in his hunting clo'e's, waiting for him.

'Well, it appears that one morning when he got there, the Squire wasn't standing stamping on the doorstep a-looking at his watch. So grandad waited. Arter a while, he rung the bell, but afore anybody could answer it, Squire throwed his bedroom winder up, and shoved his head out still wearing his nightcap, and see grandad and the 'osses waiting there. It seems as he'd been drinking 'eavy the night afore, and had forgot to wind his watch up. First of all, he roared at grandad for not waking him sooner. Then he clawed 'old of his watch, what were telling the wrong time, and shook his fist at it. "You two-faced liar," he yelled at it. "I'll teach you to play your damned tricks on me!" and he took it by the chain and bashed the watch as 'ard as ever he could on the window sill, till the bits o' glass and all the works scattered down round grandad on the gravel. "Bugger such liars as that," Squire yelled, and swacked the chain and the case somewheer back into the house.

'Then he bawled for his man to come and help him to dress. The poor chap were standing outside his bedroom door, frit to go in. He opened the door carrying the riding boots as 'e'd been polishing, and started to take the jacks out of 'em. Soon as ever he set the boots down, Old Squire got old of 'em and took 'em to the window.

' "You Bee's," he yelled. "What are you doing here at this time o' day? You ought to a-bin gone hours ago!" and out o' the window they went. "Keep going!" he hollered at them, when they landed in the rose garden.

'There were a big oak tree in the middle o' the front yard, then—it's gone now. Grandad and the 'osses were standing a' one side on it, where the Squire all'us used to mount. He could 'ear the rumpus still going on in the bedroom, 'cos Squire hadn't bothered to shut the window. Arter a minute or two, the Squire's breeches come a-bundlin' through the winder, and catched up in the oak tree. Then his pink hunting coat follered, and hung itself on the next branch. After that there were a bit of a lull in the shouting and swearin', but afore he'd finished dressing there were five white hunting stocks laying on the gravel.

'Next minute Squire stood on the porch looking a real picture, with his crop in his 'and and a smile on 'is face as if butter wouldn't melt in his mouth. His man were dancing about behind him, trying to pick the stocks up. He were eyeing the breeches and the coat, and wondering how he were going to get 'em down, when Squire turned round and give him a sovereign.

' "Leave 'em, Jarvis," he said. "I put 'em up there, an' I'll get 'em down when I'm ready." They hung there till they rotted, so grandad said. It didn't make no difference to Squire—they reckon 'e were nearly a millionaire then. But he drunk more and more, and took to gambling. One night he gambled the farm away, field by field, and then the Hall, bit by bit till everything had gone, so they say.

'Then he went home whistling as cheerful as a cricket, ate about a pound and a half o' beefsteak for his supper and washed it down with a bottle o' claret. Off he goes to bed, still whistling and singing, an' they found 'im dead next morning, sleeping like a baby. My old grandad reckoned as he'd knowed all that day that this time 'ad come. He hadn't got chick nor child to leave nothing to, only a forty-second cousin as 'ad been rubbing 'is 'ands for years at the thought o' what 'e was going to get one day. So according to my old grandad, the old chap had made up his mind to have one more good night's sport with what he'd got left, afore he hopped the twig. Ah! Things were different up at Campion's Hall in them days!'

They certainly were different now. Major Bristowe had been an officer in the Guards during the war, but one without the patrimony to keep it up once peace was declared. While he was looking round for a means of subsistence, he had chanced to meet the wealthy widow of a brother officer. The Major had acquired a wife and a readymade family almost before he was aware of it. His new wife was not his social equal, being the daughter of the heir to a countrywide hardware business. Bristowe chose to ignore it as far as he could, but it was difficult to do so in town, where the name of his wife's family leapt at him from a shop front in every other street. When Campion's Hall came on to the market, it had seemed the answer to a prayer. The life of a wealthy country squire for that of a Guards officer kept going by hardware seemed no bad exchange.

Since the old squire's death long before the war, the farm had been let to another farmer, but the house had not been occupied, and the stables had long been empty. The Bristowes had seized on its possibilities. They would step into the place the last squire had vacated, in more ways than one.

Unfortunately for him, the Major knew nothing of The System, and therefore reckoned without it. Though many years had passed since his death, the memory of the eccentric squire was still held in warm remembrance and respect. No newcomer could buy his way into The System. He would be judged by every eye, every ear, every tongue. If he passed the test, it would be as if there had never been a gap in continuity. If he did not, he would remain 'the new chap up at Campion's Hall' for ever.

It is a matter of mystery amounting almost to magic, how country folk manage to acquire details of private lives that nobody has ever wittingly disclosed. Strangers from afar though they were, before the Bristowes had resided at Campion's a week the circumstance that had led them there was common knowledge.

' 'E ain't no farmer,' George Willis informed the company at The Star. 'F'om what I've heard, 'e wou'n't know a set o' Parmitty harrers from a choking rod! Been in the army all his life till now. One o' them bloody gentlemen farmers'. The scorn in his voice made further comment unnecessary.

'I've heard as he don't have a penny to call his own,' Mrs Watson confided to Phoebe Stokes, who charred for her twice a week. 'It's all her money. An' them children ain't his, either. They go by a different name—Warrington or some such. I doubt if they'll be there long, dearie me O, that I do.'

'They say as 'e's got a man coming to run the farm for 'im,' Mrs Bluett informed all within fifty yards of her. 'A sort of general factotalum, is what my brother said. One o' them chaps as 'as bin to college.'

'Have you seen 'er yet?' Sally Watts asked May Quinton. 'My cousin has, and she told me. Talk about a madam, accordin' to our Bessie. Dressed to death an' killed wi' fashion, mincin' along with 'er nose stuck up. Bessie said she looked as if she didn't know which way her behind hung. But she ain't a lady—well, not a proper one. Her father used to work in a shop, so they say. An' I have heard as her grandfather were a tinker, as used to travel the roads mending kettles and pots.'

Even the Professor was roused to comment by his sister's interest and unending speculation. 'He may turn out to be good value. Suspend your judgment, as Polonius advises. "Modeste tamen et circumspecte judicio de tantis viris pronunciandum est. . ." ' his voice tailed off in mid-quotation, as it usually did, lacking comprehending response. The auguries for Campion's Hall in future were not good.

3 Time heals all

The depression had hit hard, but its effect had been worse on some farms than others. Ultimate survival or the alternative of bankruptcy had depended on all sorts of factors, and was decided in some cases by the minutest of details that in normal times would be taken in their stride—a cow slipping calf, an outbreak of influenza or a local shortage of binder twine in a spell of good harvesting weather. Those who had been best established when the rot set in were the ones most likely to survive, but this rule was not infallible.

The Woodwards had been at Pellmell, and the Townsends at Dindle, for many generations, across two hundred years at least, though the Tudor chimneys of Pellmell had looked down on the building of the farmhouse at Dindle in the days of William IV. It seemed likely that both lines would soon peter out, for neither farmer now possessed the brood of strapping sons that in the past had given the land a supply of loving labour. Pellmell had lost two sons in the war, and had never really recovered from the blow, materially or morally. The boys had volunteered in the first flush of patriotism, not pausing to think how much more valuable to their country their skill on the land would have been than their deaths in the trenches. Jim Woodward still had left his youngest child, another son; but nature had cast this boy into a very different mould from his dead brothers. He was of so slender a frame and so delicate a constitution that only sheer willpower kept him at work side by side with the men. Willpower and necessity perhaps, for young Jim had simply had to take the load of responsibility when one after another calamity befell the farm and its household.

During the war, he had only been a boy; but at that time there had been his grandfather, as spry at seventy as many a man at forty, his father, seemingly tough and strong, an uncle, unmarried and a bit slow on the uptake, but sturdy, and an aunt who could, and did, do a man's work; and his mother had cooked, cleaned, washed and served for them all. In spite of difficulties, the war years had been prosperous ones, with a steady demand and good prices for anything the farm could produce. The deaths of the two sons had sent the family at Pellmell, and their fortunes, sliding steadily downhill. The mother, consumed by grief, had developed arthritis, which had soon confined her to her wooden chair at the corner of the table in the farmhouse kitchen. Her sister Peggy, a war widow, whose heart lay in her work with the animals and the poultry outside, had been forced to take over the household duties. She resented the change, and loathed the indoor work. The hearty landgirl had turned into a reluctant skivvy with a biting tongue that did nothing to relieve growing misery. She was much missed on the farm, and the yard work now had to be shared among the menfolk. Grandad was getting slower and a bit difficult to work with, mainly owing to his severe deafness. The whole burden had to be carried by Jim, Young Jim, and Uncle Walter.

It was at this difficult juncture that world recession and post-war depression began to stretch out its long fingers towards farms and farming. Nothing very noticeable, at first—a strange reluctance in corn and potato dealers to pay for produce already delivered, and an even greater reluctance to bargain for more; a gradual but persistent rise in the cost of setting the land again for next year's harvest, and exorbitant demands for the necessities of the minute, such as cowcake, or coal for a much needed threshing, which now would only be delivered for cash on the nail. Labourers wanted increased wages to keep up with increased food prices. Urged by their wives, they made diffident requests that could not be ignored. Thirty shillings a week would not keep man and wife and five children, however many side benefits such as free cottage, free milk, homegrown vegetables and a pig in the backyard might be added. Their demands were modest, and made with apologies because they had no real wish to embarrass their bosses at this time of financial stringency, or to 'make bad blood' where none had ever before existed. There was no bad blood at Pellmell. What was yielded was yielded grudgingly only because the extra shillings were no longer there to grant. A bad harvest or two—the inevitable result of poor seed and scanty labour—gave the next push down the slippery slope. Jim worried himself about the state of his farm and his finances until the sound of the postman's bike on the gravel brought him out in a cold sweat and he had much difficulty in opening any letter lest it should be a bill that he could not pay, or a cold note from his bank manager drawing his attention to the precarious state of his balance. So far, he had managed never to stand on the carpet with his cap in his hand, asking for an overdraft. When that time came, it would be to admit defeat.

He was, in fact, already defeated by the worry. The pain across his diaphragm had grown in persistence and intensity until his main meal consisted of nothing but bread and milk flavoured with salt and pepper. Even the pat of butter that he was wont to add in the past now rested uneasily on his stomach. Then one day the ulcer had perforated, and Jim was picked up from an outlying field and taken to hospital in Reggie Pettigrew's car. It was long before he sat again in his saggy old armchair facing his arthritic wife across the kitchen range. He was now a victim of pernicious anaemia, and his working days were over. To struggle out into the yard exhausted all his strength, and more and more he relapsed into introspective, silent immobility. Young Jim was left to carry on alone.

Yet, in spite of crisis after crisis, Pellmell had survived. The ancient farmhouse, once so serene and beautiful, fell into chronic disrepair that was by no standards picturesque. The garden was an untended mass of weeds and unpruned roses among which hens clucked and scratched without let or hindrance, fences long since having given way to the force of muzzle-questing bullocks and back-scratching pigs. The sheds and barns sagged under rotting thatch that no longer kept out wind or rain. Every shower now rotted it farther, and every breezy day enlarged the rents. Sparrows nested there by the dozen, and roosted there by the hundred, twittering in chorus as they bathed themselves in the dust and chimble of disintegrating straw. Food for them was free, for access to the barn was almost too easy, apart from the fact that the birds were at liberty to share the meagre ration of tail corn thrown to the poultry. The head corn, emptied last harvest onto the floor of the barn, still lacked a buyer and a faint musty smell pervaded the whole barn.

And still Pellmell held on, keeping the whole defeatist army of economic pessimism at bay. Old Jim, as he was now called to differentiate him from Grandad Jim and Young Jim, still made his painful way downstairs every morning to sit where he could still be a spectator of, if no longer a participant in, the life of the farm. That centred more and more on the farmhouse kitchen.

It was this sort of unbroken tradition that made Pellmell still a farm, and its owner still a farmer in the terminology of the village. There was concern for the farmer, and for the land, exactly as there was love and respect for the fields as well as for the struggling farmer. There was still a workforce attached to Pellmell, few though the labourers were now, except for Old Jim's depleted family. From time out of mind at Pellmell the farmer and his family had knocked off for a brief respite and a hot drink at about 10.30 in the forenoon. If any of the workers wanted to find the boss, they presented themselves at the kitchen door, and were regaled with tea while consultation took place. It had lately become a dangerous habit. Jim and his wife, Eva, were chairbound, one each side of the hearth. They welcomed the sight of anybody at the door, and the sound of any voice. Pellmell had become the meeting pool of those with time on their hands. Any weekday morning a representative gathering could be found drinking tea or cocoa in the kitchen there. As most of the visitors were old, crippled or infirm (otherwise they would have been at work) the kitchen often resembled a canvas by an observant painter of Victorian genre—a picture symbolizing attenuated Hope struggling to shut out Despair, the wolf that howled persistently at the door.

Not that despair was often allowed over the worn wooden threshold. The voices coming through the open door were brittle with cheerfulness, and the topics of conversation were rarely those weighing so heavily on the mind.

Old Jim sat, pale-faced and drawn, hunched in his greasy old armchair. He could no longer sit comfortably in the high-backed, wooden Windsor that had been his father's and his grandfather's. Eva, on the other hand, found if difficult to sit low. The exchange of chairs had had a curious effect on the balance of the room, as if, with the depression, the focus of life had moved, and was now visibly unstable.

Grandad stood, an upright old figure with a thatch of bristly white hair, between his son and the table, blowing on a cup of strong cocoa. He belonged to a generation that rarely sat between dawn and dusk, and then only to ward off dangerous fatigue, or to replenish energy for the next spell of hard work. Being very deaf, his contributions to the conversation were generally *non sequiturs*, sometimes causing amusement, but more often causing intense irritation, as if his deafness offered him as a general whipping boy, though one who would feel no pain, because he rarely heard the rejoinders. Uncle Walt, still

wearing his old raincoat tied with binder-twine round his thin
middle, with his cap pushed back askew over his greying hair,
sat on an upright kitchen chair by the door that led to the stairs.
He leaned his head on the wall, and turned his face aside from
the company. The walls all round, about chairback level, were
decorated with patterns of grease where heads had leaned for
many a year. The patch behind Walt's chair was the biggest
and darkest, for he rarely sat anywhere else. He spoke not at
all, but wore the air of a weary patient in a hospital waiting-
room. Whatever or whoever it was that he had once waited
for, only he knew, but his whole attitude told of his dejection,
and that there was no longer joy in the waiting.

Between him and the table which was piled high with dirty
cups and saucers, Young Jim stood, too restless to sit down,
for of all of them he was by far the most conscious of time
being wasted, and with it money they could not afford to lose,
however little it was. Yet even he lingered, for it would never
do to suggest by his own behaviour that it was time for the
gathering to break up. His aunt Peggy washed up at the sink,
endlessly supplying clean crockery, and removing the dirty
ones from among last week's ironing, which Eva was attempting to do among the chaos from her chair. She could just reach
the hob in front of the open bars of the grate, against which the
flat-irons were placed to heat. Every now and then she
stretched out a thin arm to change the iron, turning the fresh
one upside down with a painful twist of her bony, arthritic wrist,
to spit on its shiny surface as a test of its readiness. The blob of
spittle glassed its way off the iron, and descended on to the
back of the blind old sheepdog whose doggy smell was only
part of the general pot-pourri. The dog rested its head on Old
Jim's foot, while his knee was occupied by a black tomcat with
unscrutable green eyes. All three had seen better times.

By the door, two chairs ranged against the wall were occupied by the only two labourers Pellmell employed, both now
too old for regular work, but good for an honest day's help in
time of emergency. When they were not at work, they visited

Pellmell every morning for a chat with Old Jim, and were welcome. So was the last figure in the picture, a small, tough man whose back had been injured years ago in an accident, so that it was now misshapen into a hump. He was neat and clean, with beautiful long-fingered hands curled round his mug of strong tea, and bright eyes, alert and twinkling as the talk flowed back and forth. He stood, because it hurt him to sit or lie. At home, when visiting, or in the pub, Timmy stood, usually listening, but now and then breaking in with a dry remark. As soon as he opened his mouth, he declared himself by his brogue to be a stranger within the gates. But here was a stranger who had long since been accepted by the village, and one who was now almost universally loved and appreciated.

His back had been injured by a fall of rock in a mine in his native Derbyshire, a mine in which he had worked after he married. Before that, he had been a farm labourer, and his whole heart was still with the land. When he had been suddenly and unexpectedly widowed, he had packed a case and walked out of his little stone cottage, seeking a casual acquaintance who had once offered him a job.

The acquaintance had been one of the smallholders, and Timmy's presence, skill and willingness to work had been the main reason for Glebe Farm not going under in the worst of the depression. He asked little, and gave much. Very few knew his surname, for he was simply 'Timmy' to everybody.

The topic of conversation was good for another half-hour yet. George Willis had been at plough the day before, and his horse had just staggered, fallen and died in its tracks.

'Poor Old George. It's a bad job, for 'im,' Old Jim said, for the fourth time.

'It is! Really, it is,' came like a silvery echo from Eva.

'That were a good 'oss, Boxer!' persisted Old Jim. 'In his prime. George can't stand many losses like that, I reckon.'

'You'd never of thought it, would you, really,' echoed Eva.

'I've never knowed it to 'appen afore,' said Bill Storey, one of the workmen. 'Do they know as what caused it?'

Young Jim was looking anxiously at the clock lying on its side among the china dogs, letter racks overflowing with recent unpaid bills, newspaper cuttings from years back, and all the other flotsam and jetsam of farm life which invariably accumulates on the high mantelpiece over the range in farm-house kitchens.

'Heart failure, the vet said.'

'Bad job! When did he die?' This from Grandad.

'Yis'day arternoon! At plough!' Bill Storey yelled. The old man looked his surprise and disapproval.

'At plough?' he said. 'What were the likes of 'im doing at plough?'

'The likes of who?' yelled Bill. 'Who d'yer mean?'

'Ploughing with a team? Where?'

'Oh dear, oh dear, Grandad! You do get a trial, sometimes,' said Eva. The rest were all shouting at Grandad. The only thing that got through the confusion to him was the name of George Willis.

'George found 'im, did 'e? I see. But I don't seem to understand why he should be ploughing with a team up at Garlick.' Used as they were to this kind of conversation with Grandad, they were now nearly as confused as he was. They dropped suddenly into defeated silence, in which Peggy clashed crocks together and gave vent to pent-up feeling.

'Silly old fool! Ought to be shot, out o' the way.' She hadn't intended to be heard, and was stung when Eva reproved her with, 'Peggy! Really!'

Grandad was quite oblivious of the tension he had caused. He swished the dregs of his cocoa round and round the bottom of his mug before sucking the last sugary drops into his mouth.

'He were a good chap. Allus come if you wanted 'im, middle o' the night or not. I doubt we shan't get another as good. Come on, my boy. Time we was gone!'

This remark was made to Young Jim.

Jim placed himself fair and square in front of the old man, and mouthed at him, to break the deadlock.

'WHO?' he said, clearly and distinctly, with full play of his lips.

The old man lip-read the question. 'Who? Why, him as is dead. The vet. I heard you say so. The vet's dead, you said. Died doing a bit o' ploughing for George Willis, up at Garlick. That's a rum'un, that is. I'm never 'eard the like.'

Grandad mumbled his way through the maze of chairs, and stepped over the doormat, where a tortoiseshell cat was blissfully giving suck to a litter of playful kittens.

'O dear!' said Eva, breaking into a giggle. 'I can't help laughing, I can't really! It'll be all over the village tonight that Mr Williams is dead. I hope he don't come to hear of it, that's all.'

'Well, he'll be right jumpy wi' 'issen when somebody tell's 'im as it inna the truth,' Timmy said. 'It puts me in mind o't time when Barney Weeks got blowed off t'side o' rockfaice wi' a charge o' dynamite e'd bin plaicing. Thei picked 'im oop in bits i' the bottom o' the quarry. Then somebody 'ad to go an' tell his wife what had happened.

'Thei sent a chap as she didna knaw, tellin' him to break shock to 'er, gentle-like. So 'e went tu't village, an' knocked on her door.

'When she answered it, he says, "Do they call thee t'widder Weeks?"

' "My name's Weeks," she said, "but I amna a widder."

' "Tha' wasna this morning," says the chap. "But tha is now!" '

The macabre humour was well understood, as the chuckles all round told. Timmy went on. 'Theer were a chap as used to travel round t'villages, selling tapes an' buttons an' the like from a cart, when I were a lad. We used to call him Dashitdamnit, 'cos 'e had to say that afore 'e could say anything else at all. So if a woman asked 'ow much it were for a knot o' taipe, 'e'd say, "Dashitdamnit lass, it's a penny!" Well, one day he left his old cart standing outside o't pub, while 'e went in to see if landlord's wife would buy owt from 'im. While 'e'd gone,

48

the poor old 'oss fell dead i' the shafts. There were soon a crowd round it, and when he came out o't pub, the poor feller 'as owned it were in a right sweat. When he couldn't kick nor coax his hoss to life again, he started to cuss it, telling the crowd 'as it never 'ad been no good, it were so full o' tricks. "But dashitdamnit," he said, "it's ne'er doon this afore!" '

Even Peggy laughed, and Timmy, catching Young Jim's eye, looked round for his cap.

'This'll ne'er get babby a new bonnet,' he said, and almost as if by the force of his will broke the session up. In spite of himself, Young Jim felt better for the human contact he had had in the last half-hour. If he could but hang on a bit longer, the tide would turn at last. There were already a few signs of it on other farms. His own time would come.

At Dindle, there were no visible signs of decay such as Pellmell displayed. It was a large farm, still in good heart, as far as fields and buildings went. The rot here was a deep, internal one. Of all the farmers and smallholders, Luke Townsend was the only one whose allegiance was to the chapel. Since the time John Bunyan had preached in the barn whose walls still stood in the farmyard, the Townsend family had stuck rigidly, even bigotedly, to any sect that opposed the Church of England and its clergy. Their freedom from domination by the strongest influence in village life had by no means cut them off from the community, and they had enjoyed being different from the rest. Their distinction had been maintained in a dozen little ways—they always married their cousins, for one thing, however much hearts might pull in a different direction.

As the generations of Townsends in the late Victorian period had been prolific in multiplying, there was no shortage of cousins, second cousins or forty-second cousins. In-breeding had so far caused no damage to the strain, though sons in the direct line were sadly lacking now. Another idiosyncrasy was that any male in the family had to be named after a book in the New Testament. The first few came out of it all right, with the permutations possible on the gospels and Timothy. Victorian parents had seen nothing strange in naming a son after the word of God, and had unblushingly declared 'Romans' 'Revelation' or 'Corinthians' when asked to name the child at its baptism. But Luke Townsend had more than eighty first cousins on his father's side, and nearly sixty on his mother's, many of whom were Townsends, as his father and mother had been born first cousins. Towards the end of the nineteenth century, there had been little choice left, and 'Cousin Col' was not, as might be reasonably surmised, a shortening of Colin, but of Colossians, as 'Thess' was similarly a diminutive of Thessalonians. Only once had there been a real rebellion, and that had happened when a female Townsend had married a forty-second cousin called Phil (short for Phillipians) Muddle. She, seeking to be as different as possible within the custom, had decided on Hebrews, which to her knowledge had never been used before, for her firstborn. The boy had simply refused to go through life as Hebrews Muddle, and had declared he was in future to be called plain Tom. And afterwards, he was called just that, the epithet, by way of reproof, never willingly left out.

The Townsend clan were, as the village would have said 'well breeched'. They inherited land and cash from former generations, because the inter-marriage meant that it never went out of the family. They were hard workers and shrewd business men, a bit 'near' when it came to expense they considered unnecessary, but generous towards the causes they believed in, and firm, fair people to work for. Education, in the past, had not ranked very high on their list of priorities. What did a boy need more than his bible and a good father's guiding hand? But Plain Tom Muddle had broken tradition by sending his boys to grammar school, and there was a rumour that the oldest was now heading for a university, and the medical profession. Luke Townsend felt the break with tradition keenly, but shrewdly acknowledged that in a world changing so fast as it was, education might prove valuable to a farmer, even to one born with good acreage in his pocket, so to speak. He had made a resolve that his own boys should follow where Plain Tom's led—except that up to the present he had only daughters. There was plenty of time, yet, but with Pellmell crumbling before his eyes he felt uneasy.

Both he and Rose, his wife, had been well endowed with land and money, and had made more during the war. It was the draining away of these reserves that was now biting so deep. Good husbandry demanded that the land must be kept in good heart, for future prosperity depended heavily on that one thing. They had no choice, while capital lasted, but to sink it, year after year, in the farm, and wait for the return that never seemed to come. Rose had already reached a stage when she advised doggedly against 'throwing good money after bad'. After all, some of it was her money.

Luke knew nothing but farming, and every instinct bade him hold on till the tide turned. But Rose hit him hard with her reasoning. What, she asked, if he were to die? What would she and the girls do, with farming in its present state? And how much would he be worth, when his will was published in the local paper?

Her last cut went deep, on all counts, because it would hurt the family's pride, as well as his own. So did the fact that she had thought proper not only raise, but to voice objections to his hard-won decisions. Townsend wives were expected to concede on every issue to their menfolk. When she decided (unilaterally) that until the depression lifted and they had replaced their reserves in the bank, there would be no more children, he felt that he had been exposed naked to the twentieth century, whereas until now the trappings and the customs of the nineteenth had kept him from the worst of the draughts.

Her way of ensuring safety from further pregnancies was to sleep in a separate room. He was a direct but simple man, and had no idea how to deal with such a situation within his household because it had no precedents, and was not a matter on which he could ask advice. His fear—one that turned him scarlet, and made him sweat with apprehension on the coldest of days—was that somehow the village gossips would learn of the marital situation. He heard, in his imagination, the guffaws at his expense in The Star, or even in the kitchen at Pellmell.

Curiously, the acute anxiety on this score relegated his worry over money to second place in his thoughts, and with clearer vision than before he began to see ways and means of dealing with his farming problems. In fact, Dindle had turned the corner.

'Luke's changed,' one of his workmen observed. 'He's allus been short-tempered, but now he'll bite your 'ead off soon as look at yer. But 'e's got his hand over the farm again, that you can tell. Dindle looks real well, this year. Shouldn't be surprised if there ain't a real bumper, come harvest.'

'F'om what I 'ear, all 'e wants is somebody to keep him warm a-nights. 'Nough to make any chap bad-tempered, to 'ave his old woman layin' the law down about that sort o' thing.'

'Ah. I'm 'eard that tale, an'all. But I don't take no notice on it. 'Ow d'yer know?'

'One o' the gals put it in her composition at school. Seems they 'ad to draw a plan o' their house, an' then write about it. She writ about her dad's bedroom an' then her mother's, and when she read it out loud, all the other kids got on to 'er till she told 'em they slep' in separate rooms.'

Just as Luke had feared. They always found out, somehow. Bitterness continued to grow in spite of the fact that farming began to look up again, for the first time in years. How could he bring the situation to an end, without losing face in his own eyes?

He employed no one but good chapel people, and allowed no work whatsoever on his farm on a Sunday, apart from feeding the animals. He and Rose attended service twice every Sunday, for the afternoon and evening worship. The

Minister, who had a large circuit, came only to dispense the sacrament once a month. All other services were taken by local preachers.

One of Dindle's labourers had recently offered himself as a local preacher, and this filled Luke and Rose with deep satisfaction. The Townsends themselves were not blessed with an easy flow of language, and were, on the whole, a tongue-tied bunch in company. In spite of their long association with the free church(es), the family had produced few followers in Bunyan's or Wesley's footsteps.

Luke regarded the fact that his second cowman was on trial as a local preacher as the next best thing to occupying the shiny varnished pulpit himself. Eddie Linsell was one of a large family all blessed with average intelligence and an unshakable, childlike faith in the message of the New Testament. Christ's exhortation to his disciples to 'witness to all nations' was for them a direct command. They had 'witnessed for the Lord' in every detail of 'the trivial round, the common task' of day-to-day living, in milking sheds and cornfields, on threshing tackles and dunghills, in skivvies' aprons and housemaids' caps, or wherever their lot in life took them; but until now, none had braved the ordeal of standing up before a congregation. Eddie had been allowed to do six weeks of probation at chapels other than his own, the Minister understanding well that his first appearance before the congregation in his own village would either make or break him.

When Luke and Rose, with their children, entered the chapel on that momentous Sunday for Eddie, they caught sight of his back straight away, for he was sitting in one of the front pews, his head buried in his hands—wrestling in spirit with his fear, his nervousness, his own unworthiness. But over all his doubts was his trust. The Lord would uphold him, would put words into his mouth and confidence in his heart. It was the waiting to begin that was the worst.

The American organ was placed in the front of the chapel, to one side of the pulpit. At the keyboard, already playing softly, was Gladys Bird, daughter of the horsekeeper at Stavesacre. The congregation was a good-sized one, dwarfed though it seemed by the dimensions of the bare white walls and varnished wooden ceiling. The only decoration, in or out, that the chapel boasted was a text behind the pulpit, where in a painted scroll appeared the legend 'WATCH AND PRAY'.

The text symbolized the difference between the face their god wore in chapel, and His other face, seen by the churchgoers. The church glowed with colour, and was mellowed by age that softened its contours and reduced its size. The chapel's uncompromising austerity dwarfed its occupants. The church was pervaded with the smell of centuries; the chapel with a smell of puritan cleanliness that rose mostly from the overpowering quantity of varnished wood. Strangely, its very bareness of line and the rigidity of its Victorian furnishings induced quite as much awe and reverence as its beautiful neighbouring temple two hundred yards distant, perhaps even more. The face the god turned towards the church was that of one who asked for beauty and praise; a loving, social god, easily appeased by age-old ritual and formal prayers. The chapel face was that of a stern god who demanded purity of heart and mind, self-denial and obedience; but that of a loving father nevertheless, at least to those who truly believed that the fear of the Lord was the beginning of wisdom. In spite of that, the chapelgoers seemed to take the actual presence of the Almighty in their midst for granted—a very present god in times of peace as well as of trouble. The preachers and prayer-leaders spoke directly into the Almighty Ear, as if in truth they already stood face to face with Him. They lifted their voices to praise Him, and dropped them again to plead; they flattered Him, only to admonish Him—even, it almost seemed at times to threaten Him, before sinking their tones once more to a whisper in order to cajole Him into forgiveness of their simple sins, or support for their humble aspirations.

To Eddie, awaiting the ordeal of going up into the pulpit, He was near enough to be touched, near enough for His unsophisticated disciple to see the wounds in the hands of the Son, or to feel the blessing from the hands of the Father, as they rested for a moment on his bare head. Near enough for a touch to fill him with the Holy Spirit, for whose Presence he had been agonizedly praying for the last ten minutes. He felt strength flow into him, though indeed the hand on his shoulder was only that of Luke Townsend, who had leaned across to give him an encouraging pat, in case his courage should be failing him at the crucial moment.

Eddie stood up, straightened his shoulders in his cheap, neat Sunday suit, and walked resolutely up the pulpit steps, standing with bowed head, until the organist brought her voluntary to an abrupt but tuneful conclusion. Then the boy in the pulpit raised his hand, and announced in a firm, clear voice: 'Let us begin our worship by joining our voices in praise as we sing together hymn 229.' He stood, a thin but sturdy slip of manhood, with his head thrown up and his straw-coloured hair sleeked back from a face pale with emotion and lit by a pair of dark, intense eyes.

> *All people that on earth do dwell*
> *Sing to the Lord with cheerful voice*
> *Him serve with mirth; His praise forth tell,*
> *Come ye before Him, and rejoice.*

There was no tremor in Eddie's voice as he read out the words, no trembling in the hand that held the hymnbook. Gladys played the first line of the melody, and struck the chord that brought the congregation to its feet. The singing, led by Gladys's soprano and Luke's heavy baritone, filled the chapel. Into it was put the relief of the whole congregation that their particular soldier in the army of Christ had at least gone over the top with daring and courage. With everything in them they willed him now to win his battle. They need not have feared. From strength to strength he went, as hymns, extempore prayers, and readings from Old and New Testaments fell away behind him in the order of the service. When he sank down to pray before beginning the sermon, Alice slipped quietly onto the organ stool, and Gladys turned to face the congregation to 'render a sacred song'. It seemed as if some of the preacher's elation had flowed out over the rival organists, for they acted for once in comradeship and accord, each, if she had been able to put it into words, offering up a bit of her proper pride as a sacrifice 'for Eddie's sake'.

'Cast your burden upon the Lord' rang pure and true through the chapel, where many an eye was already moist with emotion and the power of the music. Eddie sat up and listened. The last remnants of nervousness fell away from him as he looked down on Alice's face and Gladys's back. He felt that he was seeing both of them for the first time, though he had known them, of course, all his life. He had looked up to them, always, partly because they were women, partly because they were older by seven or eight years than he, partly because of their skill in music and their office in the chapel, but mostly because their families stood a little above his in the hierarchy. Now, he was in fact looking down on both from the pulpit's advantage, and in his new dignity as preacher, which lifted him to their level as a worshipper. When the song came to an end, Gladys turned and looked at him, and Alice, rising from the stool, sent him a smile of sweet encouragement. He rose.

Rarely had so moving a sermon been preached from that pulpit. Eddie took his text from the epistle to the Romans: 'How shall they hear, without a preacher?' Then he talked simply, about himself, his doubts, his fears, his faith, his trust, his guilty feelings at his cowardice, his terror when he had committed himself to the trial, and his apprehension of the present day, for he was aware of the truth that a prophet is not without honour except in his own country; and finally, he told them how he had, like the disciples at Pentecost, felt himself filled with the Holy Spirit, and how astonished he was at finding the gift of tongues bestowed on him. It was in God's strength and by God's grace he had felt able to stand before his elders and his betters, to witness for the Lord that the age of miracles is not yet past.

If all this was couched in ungrammatical language, there was no one there to notice, let alone to care.

The youngster who stood exalted in the pulpit was one of them, a David drawn from their own ranks to combat the Goliath of worldly sin. It was Eddie Linsell, whom they had known from babyhood, whose head was now surrounded by glory, who was speaking with the tongue of an angel, rapt in wonder, love and praise.

When he stopped speaking, and sat down, leaning his head on his hands, the silence in the building was so intense that it thrummed on the ears. Gladys and Alice sat side by side, caught in a moment of outward-giving that was greater than either of them, lifted above petty jealousy or self-esteem. In another moment, Eddie would have to rise again to say the last prayer, and announce the last hymn. Luke, raising his head in preparation, saw that their young advocate had already given his all. His face was now drained of all colour, and showed above his clasped hands like a lump of fresh-made putty. He must be given a moment's respite, lest his triumph should be spoilt by failure at the eleventh hour. Striding from his pew, to his own utter astonishment, Luke placed himself squarely in the aisle, in front of the table below the pulpit from which the sacrament was dispensed once a month. He could find no words of his own—perhaps because he did not really need to. He gave voice to the words that came unbidden to his tongue. 'All hail the power of Jesu's name,' he said, and the sigh that released the congregation's pent-up breath sounded very much like a sob, here and there.

Down in the seat in front of the organ, two minds leapt to response. Gladys pushed Alice onto the stool, and flicking with expert hands the worn *Hymnal with Tunes*, set before her the music of 'Diadem'. Alice began to play, and Gladys had just time to reach Luke's side before the congregation rose to join them in the singing. By the time they arrived at the triumphant 'Crown Him! Crown Him! Crown Him!', the women and children were all following Gladys, and the men following Luke as the magnificent melodies rolled in and out among the intricacies of the tune, in a paean of heartfelt praise.

Miss Taylor and Miss Nellie, out for a walk, stopped outside the door to listen, for both were sensitive Christians who recognized the note of utter sincerity, and had the awed sensation that for a moment they were on holy ground.

Carried by the light breeze, the sound of such hearty singing reached the Professor as he leaned at his cottage door, dreaming of the classical world in which his spirit had its being. It wrenched him back to reality, and substituted for the Ionic columns of his fantasy the tall elms, silhouetted against an autumn sunset, that framed his view.

'Bare ruined choirs, where late the sweet birds sang,' he murmured, following his own train of thought immediately with another inward vision of the ruins of Fountains Abbey as he had last seen it. He felt the link between past and present as if it were something tangible, and himself a being present through all time.

Mrs Watson, on the other side of the road, commented to her cat, 'Dearie me O, Pussy! Whatever have they got to sing so loud about?'

'Something special on at the chapel,' Uncle Bert remarked to May.

'They're certainly belting it out tonight,' said May. 'Good to hear somebody's happy with their lot.' She had just been subjected to a large dose of the Wimperris brand of socialism.

Charlie, crossing the yard between stable and cellar, paused to listen. Above him the church and churchyard stood out against the darkening sky, caught by the last yellow gleams of the sun. The clear evening air defined sharply the outline to tower, nave and chancel roof, picked out with delicate pencil strokes the tracery of every window, and blocked in the solidity of every leaning headstone.

The romantic in Charlie responded to the complementary

delights of eye and ear, acknowledging the sweet chance that had brought him outside at that moment and caught him so squarely between two aspects of the many ways men have invented to keep themselves in touch with the god they have created. Across a great gap in background and culture, he reached out to share the Professor's philosophy.

A dying gleam of vivid sunlight caught one of the church windows, reflected itself there for a broken second, and immediately went out. Charlie had the feeling that the church had winked an aged eye at him, as if to say, 'See? When you're my age, it's all one, anyway!'

> Gabriel John lies under this stone
> He died in the year one thousand and one . . .

'Tis all one, to Gabriel John. 'Tis all one! 'Tis all one! Church and chapel, summer and winter, dawn and dusk, rain and shine, triumph and disaster, birth and death . . . to the life of a village, 'tis all one. Individual joys and private sorrows are lost in time like raindrops in the ocean, or specks of dust in a ploughed field. Yet the ocean is made up of raindrops, and the field of specks of dust.

Luke Townsend shared his wife's bed that night, and the village folded them, reunited, into its stillness.

4 March, many weathers

Spring was late, held waiting in the wings while winter made one last appearance after another with a flurry of snow, a biting north wind, a weekend of driving rain, and a succession of damp, foggy mornings. March had not lived up to its reputation of coming in like a lion and going out like a lamb. Instead, it had done its best to repeat November, with bleak, raw fogs through which the sun barely penetrated, even at midday. When the April sun did at last break through, everything sprang into life at once, especially in the woods and fields.

Reg Pettigrew of Stavesacre took the opportunity on the first bright clear morning to walk his farm. There was little in life that gave him greater satisfaction, or more enduring pleasure. He was an uncomplicated and somewhat ingenuous man, who seized pleasure where he found it, which was usually in the simple things of his everyday life.

He was whistling as he stumped along the cart track between the ploughed field and the edge of the woodland, a tuneful rendering of 'Look for the silver lining' which had been put into his mind by a cloud hanging in the breezy blue of the April sky. His tall figure was made to appear shorter than it really was by the sturdy breadth of his shoulders under the baggy tweed jacket, and the extraordinary width of the breeches at the thigh. Below the knee, the light lacing of the breeches and the snug fit of leather leggings and boots showed slender, well-shaped legs. Under the shapeless tweed hat, a pair of keen grey eyes looked out from a weathered, Indian-red face, and took in every detail, from the clouds hanging above the horizon to the daisies in the grass at this feet. He had come out to view his crops, but he missed no change in the light, no fresh formation of cloud, no tree uncurling its first few leaves, no bird or rabbit in search of provender. He carried a double-barrelled gun in the crook of his left arm, but it was not loaded. It was taken along more out of habit than for possible use, because Reg never killed at random or just for the sake of killing, though he was an excellent shot, and like most countrymen enjoyed an organized shoot as much as anyone else. He farmed for a living, but he farmed with the soul of an artist, and the sight of a twenty-acre field of standing corn rippling to the breeze gave him quite as much pleasure aesthetically as the calculation of its yield gave him in terms of cash. If one had asked him what his religion was, he would have answered that he was a sort of Christian, though 'he'd be blowed if he knowed' what sort. The Professor would have argued that he was a devotee of Demeter. Reg himself had probably never heard of the goddess, at least since he left school.

The whistled tune came to an end as he reached a five-barred gate that led from farm to woodland, and he stopped. He leaned the gun upright against the gatepost, picked a couple of primroses from under the hedge, and cupped them in his hands as he leaned his elbows on the top bar of the gate. The flowers held his attention for at least two minutes, and he marvelled yet again at the delicacy of the creamy-yellow colouring, the precision of the overlap of heartshaped petals, and the pale, pale green of the calyx as it ran into the even paler green of the fragile stalk. The warmth of his hands brought out the delicate fragrance, the very essence of spring, he thought, and he held the flowers to his nose for a second or two before carefully fitting them into the buttonhole in the lapel of his jacket. Then he gave his attention to the trees.

The silver birch and hazels still dangled weather-worn catkins, and the beeches were just breaking into delicate leaf on their dark, web-thin twigs. An oak here and there glowed pink with its unfolding leaves and curious, bulbous little flowers. To one side of the gate, in the hedge, was a huge elm, still bare of leaf at the top, but bushing out round the bole with feathery young leaves, like a feather-legged old hen; on the other side, ten yards or so from the gate, an ash stood smooth, grey-green and solid, with no sign yet of leaf, though its soot-black buds were swelled nearly to bursting among the bunches of brown keys left from last autumn.

'Oak before ash, only a splash,' said a wheezy voice behind him. Rapt in his pleasure at flowers and trees, Reg had not noticed the approach of Sam Gaskin. The old man had spent all his working life on Stavesacre, giving up work only when Reg took the farm over. He was now over eighty, and walked with the help of a strong ashplant; but he could not keep away from the land, and still plodded down from the village whenever the weather was fine. It was his birthright, in a spiritual sense, and he felt the familiar fields to be his quite as much as the Duke's (whose property they were legally) or Reg's who farmed them as a tenant farmer. Reg had welcomed him from the first, partly because he enjoyed the old man's tales and reminiscences, partly because he had enough sense to take advice from so knowledgeable a source.

'Ah, I hope you're right, Sam,' Reg replied. 'We had enough rain in February to last us a bit, I reckon. But March wasn't too bad.'

'Wasn't a good March though,' said Sam. 'Not enough wind to dry things up. "A peck o' March dust is worth a king's ransom", my old Dad used to say. 'An 'e were right. Besides, it stands to reason you've got to 'ev March. You may not get it till June to be sure, but you've got to 'ev March.'

Reg's eyes twinkled. He appreciated Sam.

'I like to see a man walkin' round his farm,' Sam went on. 'My old dad used to say no other muck were half as good as the farmer's boots. What are you putting in Furlong this year?' Sam always used the age-old names for the fields; Reg had learned them from him while the rest of the men he had taken over with the farm were still being reticent about accepting him as their boss.

They had few precedents about placing a tenant farmer, because this was the first time the Duke had ever let the home farm of the Priory Estate. Until then, it had been farmed for him by his agent.

'Barley,' answered Reg. 'I want to get it drilled before the month's out.'

'Take your time, my boy, take your time. You can't hurry barley. Wait till the may's out. My dad told me that, soon as ever I went to work with him, when I were about ten year old.

When the hedge is white wi' may,
Sow your barley night an' day.
When wi' may the hedge be white,
Sow your barley day an' night.'

A blackbird swooped down, squarking its warning cry. It alighted close to them with the sudden braking of feet and tail that never failed to intrigue the nature-lover in Reg.

'Got a nest 'ere somewheer,' said Sam. ' 'E don't like us tramplin' about anywheer near it, I'll be bound.'

Reg had already begun to search the blackthorn hedge, peering at eye-level into its dim, prickly shade. He had nearly reached the ash-tree bole, when Sam's urgent voice arrested him. 'Don't you go no further,' he called. 'If I was you, I shouldn't go no further.'

Reg had not found the nest, and failed to understand the old man's agitation. Maybe there was a bit of folklore in these parts about blackbirds—as Reg knew, there was some taboo or ritual observance attached to nearly everything, though the

63

younger folk took little notice of the old customs now.

Reg came out of the ditch under the hedge, and went back to Sam.

'Why not?' he asked. 'Will my eyes drop out, or my nose fall off or something, if I poke it into a blackbird's business?'

The old man was disturbed, as Reg could see. 'It don't do to make fun, Mr Pettigrew, sir,' he said with dignity, 'though the likes o' you 'as got no call to listen to the likes o' me I know. But you ain't one to laugh, in the ordinary way, I'll say that! You can't ha' been here seven year or more without somebody tellin' you 'bout that tree!' Sam's stick was raised, pointing at the ash.

'What's wrong with the tree?' Reg asked. 'No, nobody's ever said anything to me about it.'

'Ah. Well, you'll find out, one o' these days, if you don't keep well away from it. There's folks in this village as 'ould go five mile round 'fore they'd walk underneath it. An' I'll bet you ain't ever seen one o' your men setting under it to eat 'is grub.'

'No, I haven't, come to think about it. But there's plenty of other trees. I never took no notice.'

'They don't call it "the 'anging tree" for nothing.'

'Oh, I see. Somebody strung 'isself up there at one time, did 'e?'

'Not as I know of,' said Sam with dignity. 'Jes' keep away f'om it, Sir. That's all. I'll be a-going.' He hobbled off, while Reg surveyed the ash tree with a puzzled gaze. He might make light of old Sam's warning in broad daylight, but the truth was that he had his own full measure of rural superstition, and was not the bravest of men once the sun had gone down.

His family for generations had had a reputation of being folks with 'the gift of seeing'. The women in particular never tired of relating their experiences with the supernatural, and though the men might scoff and make fun of the more outrageous of the women's tales, there were plenty of authenticated accounts from well-respected members of the clan to make them a bit uneasy on their own behalf. Pettigrew men had to admit that they would never be exactly surprised to find themselves face to face with a departed spirit at any moment.

Reg had not scoffed, because his simple, sensitive mind could not account rationally for one or two queer occurrences that he remembered from his own youth. His younger brother, Geoff, had told him a tale or two as well that he didn't care to disbelieve, at least openly. But the two brothers had been out of their native district for a long time now, and the influence of aunts and uncles was wearing thin.

They were the sons of a prosperous smallholder on the edge of the fenlands. After the war, when Reg had married, they had taken the plunge of their lives, and applied for the tenancy of a derelict highland farm—Stavesacre. The Duke's own family had fallen apart, during the war, and when the conflict was over he had realized that things would never be the same again. He had leased The Priory to the local public school, and moved his own possessions into The Lodge. Then he had decided to let the home farm, and its farmhouse, Stavesacre. To free the farmhouse, he had been forced to evict his estate manager, rehousing him in one of the houses in the village.

Reg and Geoff had been the tenants selected, because of their knowledge of farming and the proof they could give that they had some capital to keep going with until the farm should begin to pay.

Derek Marston, the agent, was the only aggrieved one in the whole transaction. With the Duke so often away, he had been the virtual boss of the Priory Estates, and had enjoyed the position of a landed gentleman, to all intents and purposes. Suddenly, he had found himself only an agent again, with the Duke more often up at The Lodge to keep an eye on him, and the well-stocked game reserves he had thought of as his own practically denied to him. He was not a native of the village, and had never exerted himself to be a real part of it, though he had his place in its hierarchy as 'the Duke's man'. His chagrin at the changes could not be vented on the Duke; but as agent, he had plenty of opportunity of venting it on the newcome Pettigrew brothers. He had persuaded the Duke to keep all the Stavesacre woodland for his own use as game coverts. This meant that Marston and his gamekeepers had free access to the farm when and how they chose. The tenancy agreement denied the farmers any right of way in the woods, or any shooting rights on the farm itself.

This arrangement did not really bother the Pettigrews, except for a slight irritation at the feeling of being watched, and a natural desire to enjoy forbidden luxury now and again by taking a pot shot at the noisy pheasants, which strolled through the garden, got under their feet in the farmyard and occasionally came uninvited into the kitchen.

The partnership agreement between the brothers had not long survived their move. This was chiefly because of the mutual dislike between Geoff and Reg's wife, Gwen. After the first few struggling years, they had amicably agreed to part company, as far as farming went. Reg re-negotiated the tenancy in his own name, and helped Geoff set up as a contractor and haulier. Both ventures were now on a reasonably sound financial footing, and there was chance for mutual assistance on a 'strictly business' basis.

'It's another case o' what my great-uncle Stivvie said, now,' Reg had told Charlie, down at the pub. 'My old grandfather owed his brother for a wheelbarrow load o' mangolds he'd had to borrow, one time. Stivvie made it clear he didn't want the debt paid in mangolds back again 'cos he'd got more than he knowed what to do with. But he kept overing with it every time he met grandad. Grandad couldn't really believe his own brother meant to charge him for such a skerrick of help. But he was stung one day into asking Stivvie how much he owed him. Stivvie scratched his head, trying to work it out. Then he said, "A shilling." Grandad was flabbergasted. "A whull *shilling?*" he said.

'Stivvie nodded. "Yis," he said. "Bugger brothers. If you're got anything to give 'em, give 'em it. If you ain't, charge 'em well for it. I ain't got nothing as I want to give away to nobody." '

The brothers' decision had been a sound one. Geoff came and went at Stavesacre as he pleased, always willing to help, and always welcomed by everybody except Gwen. Even she masked her jealousy of the place Geoff held in the affection of her husband and children, because she was nothing if not hardheaded, and understood the value of the new relationship in terms of money. With Geoff out of the farm proper, she had no one to curb her ambition, which was to be a lady—by which she really meant to have enough money to indulge expensive tastes, and to climb the rural social ladder.

Geoff disliked her—particularly her put-on airs and graces, and her barely concealed contempt of Reg for his unwillingness to keep pace with her social ambitions. She felt that her intelligence and business acumen, to say nothing of her feminine charm, were all wasted. Reg was too satisfied with his lot, and never expected to be anything but a working farmer. He put on no airs, and hated to be dragged behind Gwen to dances, balls and other functions where he felt out of his social depth; but such 'do's' were the breath of life to Gwen, and he acted often, though unwillingly, as her escort. His shy, unassuming presence was, however, always welcome everywhere, and he was universally liked where Gwen was only tolerated because she was his wife. He and Geoff had slipped into the village as if they had been born there, though it was some time before their place in the social hierarchy was completely established. As it turned out, what was accorded them was a kind of mezzanine floor between smallholders and farmers proper. That suited Reg perfectly, but Gwen fought on doggedly for a place on the fringe of the layer of society that included the professionals, as well as the upper grades of the local farming community—the doctors, vets, teachers at the public school, bank managers—the people, in fact, who went to the Masonic ball once a year, and wore dinner jackets for the occasion.

Reg and Geoff still spoke the broad dialect of their native region, much to Gwen's humiliation. (She had cultivated a 'posh' accent that highlighted her frequent grammatical mistakes in a fashion most embarrassing to her more educated acquaintances.) Reg resolutely refused to change his speech, in spite of her nagging corrections of his language, which were often wrong, anyway. She did manage to get him into a dinner suit, though he told her it was like dressing a pig in pink satin. On the first occasion that he wore it, he danced round the kitchen table with exaggeratedly mincing gait, quoting 'You'll never make a gentleman o' me, John', to the delight of his sons.

They had four children, well spread out, since Gwen had never really wanted any. Still, she loved them after her fashion, and they owed their education to her ambition, though to be fair to Reg he also appreciated the advantages it could offer in the post-war period. He adored his children, in his way. He would have given himself up to torture to save one of the girls a tear or one of the boys a heartache. He was proud beyond measure of his daughter Margaret, now eighteen and a good looker who had been to a grammar school, and who could play, it seemed, any instrument that fell into her hands, though she excelled on the piano. She was skilled in all kinds of ways with her hands, and enjoyed making things, especially clothes. There was a continual battle of words nowadays between her and her mother, which every now and then rose to the level of a bitter quarrel. Reg dreaded the scenes between them more than any other thing. It was to avoid these outbreaks of mutual jealousy that he took the line of least resistance with Gwen, and followed meekly in her wake when she dragged him as unwilling escort to social occasions. He had long ago worked out that the main reason of her discontent was the element of rivalry now presented by another full-grown, pretty, accomplished and (worst of all) younger woman in the house. She wanted to do everything that Margaret did, to live again through her daughter the years she had

68

missed by being married too young to a man she had never really understood, or to be truthful, cared much for. She could still wrap him round her little finger, however, and that compensated for a good deal.

Roderick, their twenty-year-old son, was the spit-image of his uncle Geoff, and a chip off the Pettigrew block with a vengeance. So, indeed, were the other two, Roly, now thirteen, and Angela, only three. Roly had been a grudging concession to Reg, who hated 'not having a baby about the place'. Angela had been a mistake, and one that Gwen never let Reg forget. Margaret, Roddy and Roly had all been delightful, docile, tractable children with dark hair, grey eyes and olive skins handed down by their father.

When she had realised to her horror that she was once again pregnant, Gwen had comforted herself by the thought that after so long a gap—nearly ten years—the pattern might have changed. She had indulged in a good deal of daydreaming as the months had passed, telling Reg continually that this one was going to be *her* child—a fair-haired, cream-skinned, blue-eyed, delicately-boned girl who would have to have dancing lessons as soon as she was old enough. 'A little princess,' she would say. 'I'm going to call her Angela— my golden-haired, blue-eyed little angel.'

'Angela!' snorted Reg. But he hoped and prayed with all his heart that she might get the child she wanted this time. Perhaps if she did it would cure some of her wilder schemes for keeping herself socially in the swim, like having a maid living in. They worried him.

'It's a girl,' Nurse Hardy had announced to him, and he had breathed out a great sigh of relief. Fifteen minutes later, he had allowed the nurse to lead him to the bedroom.

'Come on, wake up, Mrs Pettigrew,' Nurse had said to the drowsy Gwen. 'Don't you want to show your husband the baby?' She had laid the bundle in Gwen's arms, and Gwen had pulled back the shawl. She took one look at the red, wizened little face, and began to cry. Then she pushed the baby into

Reg's arms and shrieked. 'Take her away! I never want to see her again!'

The baby was indeed uglier than most newborn humans usually are, which is saying a good deal. She was very red, very wrinkled, with a large mouth that was already twisted, it seemed to Reg, into a sardonic grin. She opened her eyes for a fraction of a second, and it had seemed to her father that he had been shot through with a blue-black arrow; and her hair, a great mop of it growing well down into her neck, was the colour and texture of a North-American Indian's. The longed-for angel child had turned out to be a proper little witch.

The harvest had been good. The land was really responding to good husbandry at last. Labour had been scarce though, and even with Geoff's willing help, Reg had been a little late in carting and stacking the corn. When the potatoes were ready, with a buyer waiting, he had tried to get some casual labour, but the gangs of aproned and hooded women that were part of the landscape in his native region did not operate here. Then Geoff had suggested the diddikies, and they had moved on to his land. They'd worked well, and been paid piece-work rates, which had ensured his crops being speedily gathered. But when the job was finished, they had stayed on, finding one excuse after another for not departing when requested, then told, and finally ordered to do so.

Just before Christmas, however, Reg had seen the welcome sight of the string of caravans, horses and lurchers pass by Stavesacre windows towards the main road. The Christmas season was well over before he discovered that one family had stayed behind. He had sent Roddy over to investigate, and the boy brought back disturbing news. All the vans had gone, but a couple with 'a whull hustle' of kids had set up house in the derelict cottage on the far side of the woods. The cottage was very remote from the village, but it was still on the edge of the farm, though two hundred acres or so of the Duke's game reserves lay between it and the farmhouse. The cottage was not fit for human habitation, and indeed had been condemned many years before. The diddikies would have to be evicted— but Reg was not at all sure how the law stood on such an issue. In any case, while winter had lasted so severely, he could not bring himself to turn them out. Now, with summer round the corner, he had no choice. Besides, he guessed they would soon bring about their own undoing by poaching. What he did not want was that they should bring about his, too.

The village itself had already begun to murmur again. Reg had sensed a strong undercurrent of protest when he had first employed the diddikies; now it was being put into words, as eggs, chicken, firewood and other portable goods took to disappearing in the hours of darkness, according to the tales he heard.

He made up his mind to skirt the wood the whole way round, while still out, and see for himself what the situation at the cottage was.

He walked on, pausing every now and then to stand and gaze at the gently rolling fields, or to listen to a thrush's song. He stood motionless to watch a litter of baby rabbits scampering about round their doe, intrigued and delighted by their fluffy newness, while registering nevertheless some uneasiness at their numbers. A dog fox, loping across a wheat-field, like a streak of russet in a green carpet, soothed his concern. You could almost always rely on old dame Nature to keep a fair balance, if you didn't interfere too much.

It was while he stood still for a minute or two that he first became aware of movement on the other side of the hedge. When he stopped, the movement stopped. This happened several times. When the next gate in the hedge came into view, he drew near to it at a leisurely pace, then dropped his gun, sprinted the few yards to the gate, put his hand on top of it and vaulted over with a sideways leap learned long ago but now rarely used. He found himself looking down, not on one of the diddiki family, as he had suspected, but on one of the Duke's gamekeepers. He was angry—there was no need for them to watch him on his own land as if he were a poacher, even if he did happen to be carrying a gun.

'What's your game?' he asked bluntly, as the man straightened up and came out from under the hedge. 'What do you reckon you're doing, spying on me from under a hedge, an' trying not be seen?'

'I've got my orders,' said the man—the assistant keeper, one whom Reg knew very well.

'What orders? Whose orders?'

'Mr Marston's. Somebody's been doing a nice lot o' poaching round about here. Snares everywhere, an' traps. Disturbin' the hen pheasants, and I don't know what all.'

'Well, it ain't me, and you know it ain't,' said Reg, 'so clear off. I don't want you following me!'

'You clear off,' retorted the keeper. 'It's you as is trespassing. You're on the wrong side o' the 'edge, mate, on His Grace's land. Keep to yer own side. An keep yer bloody diddiki friends on your side, an' all, else there'll be trouble.'

'There'll be trouble if you talk to me like that,' said Reg, nettled. It was a long time since anyone had taken that tone to him. 'There's two can play at that game. If you keep off my land as well as I keep off the Duke's, we shan't get in each other's way a lot. But you start making trouble, an' I'll lay as I can find ways o' getting level. An' you can tell Marston that from me.'

He climbed the gate slowly, and picked up his gun. So Marston was going to declare open war at last, was he? Using the diddikies as an excuse. Reg's jaw set. He wouldn't turn them out now—well, not for a week or two.

The keeper had followed him to the gate, and stood leaning on the other side of it. Strictly speaking, both were now on ground where they had every legal right to be. In the seven years or more of Reg's tenancy, this was the first time the hidden animosity of Marston and his men had ever broken the surface, though Reg had often had to bite his tongue at Marston's tone of patronizing insolence. (He always called Reg 'Pettigrew', without prefix—much as the squire might have spoken to his groom in days gone by.) Reg was trying to make up his mind whether to march silently off, leaving the field to the keeper but keeping the peace, or to simply stand and stare him out, till he had to retire defeated. He had decided on the former as the better way of maintaining his own clean record as a sensible, reasonable man to work with, when the keeper spoke again.

'Mr Marston said if I see you, I was to tell you to get them bloody diddikies off the Duke's land afore His Grace gets back again.'

'You tell Marston from me I'll keep 'em as long as I want 'em on my farm,' Reg replied.

'Your farm! How long 'as it been your farm? Bloody jumped up shit 'eels tenant farmer! A real farmer 'ould never have had the diddikies to start with. I shall say so to His Grace, fust chance as I get. They'll get their marching orders then, by goles they will. You wan't to look out you don' get yours, an' all!'

He turned and went off among the trees. Reg was shaking now with suppressed fury. Beware the anger of a patient man! Nine-tenths of Reg's character was that of a pacifist always ready to sink his own pride rather than quarrel with anyone. The tenth part was an Irish temper inherited from his maternal grandfather. It would lie dormant for months, even years, sometimes. Then something suddenly pressed the spring, and up it came like a jack-in-the box, nearly choking Reg with its strength and fury.

The warmth seemed to have gone out of the sun. He no longer saw anything but Marston's supercilious face, as it would be when the keeper reported the encounter. Very well; if it was to be war, Reg would have to be sure to win it; but he would never again demean himself by bandying words with a gamekeeper. He would make the first move, sending Roddy tonight with a polite request for Marston to fetch the broods of young pheasants his broody hens had reared, and which his family had fed and cared for. He had no obligation to help the keepers in this way. Until now it had been done as a neighbourly favour. As he had told the keeper, two could play at being obstropolous. He began to enjoy the thought of pitting his wits against la-di-da Marston's. The merry twinkle in his eyes was replaced by a glitter that seemed to shoot red sparks into the soft air. Roddy and Geoff would enjoy it, too. The only fly in the ointment was the Duke's uncertain reaction, if he ever got to hear about it. Reg's tenancy was safe for another two years, but he hoped it would then be renewed, even if at an increased rent. He'd always got on very well with His Grace till now, but he had to admit that he might possibly be on dangerous ground if the Duke supported Marston. Them as lived longest 'ould see most. He trudged on, giving the cottage a wide berth after all. His next move would be to offer the diddiki a proper job, permanent if some other accommodation could be found for the family. At present he would not raise that issue, knowing how long it would take for the council to get round to doing anything about it. But he would have to threaten the bloke with instant sacking if poaching still went on, or theft from the village. A sudden instinct bade him consider from whom, in the village, tales of the thefts had come. They could nearly all be traced back to households in Marston's employ. He found himself looking forward to a game of chess played on the chequerboard of Stavesacre's fields and woods, with the diddikies and under-keepers as the pawns.

He began to whistle again, and strode off purposefully towards home and lunch time. He paused for the last time, good humour fully restored, to look at the village lying below him, and at the white walls of Stavesacre gleaming in the sunshine among the trees that surrounded it. One day, he thought, he'd get his paint-box out again, and paint that view

as he could see it now. He took up his tune again, this time
breaking into song.

'With a wing, wang, waddle O!
Bridle and saddle O!
Send the boys toddle O
After the plough.'

5 The hand that rocks the cradle . . .

The Mothers' Union met on the afternoon of the second Tuesday in the month, and the Women's Institute on the evening of the first Wednesday. This arrangement had a significant effect on the membership of each body. The only meeting-place available without considerable cost was the schoolroom. There were other public places, such as 'the room' at The Star, the chapel room, and a very small church hall. But as these were not in constant use, they were cold, even in the summer months, and two out of the three had not yet been connected to the electricity supply, because of a lack of cash. Then there was a hiring fee to be found, even for a small meeting, and a cleaner to be paid afterwards. The local education authority did, however, recognize the Women's Institute as an educational body, and the amount paid for a WI meeting in the school was only nominal. The MU could have had free use of the church hall, but it was a cold, bare, cramped little place; so for a long time their monthly meeting had been held in the Enrolling Member's sitting-room. Each member brought something towards the refreshments consumed at 3.45 pm, and the meeting broke up at 4.15 pm. This timing had a sort of refining effect on the gathering, since it excluded any who 'worked for their living', that is, who were in the regular employ of someone else. It also excluded those who had very small children, because infant school closed at 3.30, and though babies in arms (or prams) were welcome, toddlers wanting their tea tended to become disruptive. The effect was to confine the membership of the MU to unmarried ladies, widows, and those whose children were off their hands—though in fact few of the last seemed interested. Consequently, there was certainly something of an 'elite air' about the MU.

The Women's Institute had the advantage of meeting when small children were in bed, and husbands at home to take care of the others. Not all husbands were well disposed towards it, however. There was something vaguely sinister to a great many of the men about a gathering of women that had no religious attachments, or party political ones, but which nevertheless now and again poked its finger into regional or even national affairs that men regarded as their province. The main aim of the MU was to uphold the sanctity of Christian marriage. That, to many men, was an entirely laudable aim, because it constrained the goose from any thought of wrongdoing (at least in theory) while not interfering with the gander at all. (Nobody seems ever to have thought of setting up a Fathers' Union with the same objective.) On the other hand, the aim of the WI was to better the lot of rural women. Many men resented this, almost as an insult. What was wrong with the lot of their women, that it should take a countrywide organization of females to better it?

Some wives acquiesced, and even agreed with their menfolks' opinion, staying well clear of such a subversive, dangerous lot as the WI. Others, whose husbands did not openly oppose it, or who in any case made this a test case for a bit of autonomy, sometimes paid dearly for their gesture of independence in a dozen little ways. Fred Johnson always referred to the WI scathingly as 'the gossip gang'; Arthur Cook flatly refused his wife permission to take anything towards the refreshments, on the grounds that women who had had a good tea didn't need an extra meal just to keep talk going; and on the occasion when bright little Millie Butler had made a Dutch apple tart for Sunday's dinner instead of the familiar apple pudding, her young husband Len had thrown such a temper that Millie had gone home to her mother for the rest of the day.

'I ain't 'aving no fancy Women's Institute tack on my table,' he bawled, picking up the tart whole and slinging it into the dog's dish. While Millie cried, Len tried to make the dog eat it—but unfortunately the animal didn't care much for either apple or cinnamon. 'See, even the bloody dog won't eat it! Don't you never try no more bloody stuff you learn up there on me!'

'O Len!' wailed Millie. 'I 'avn't got nothing else for afters!'

'Bugger such afters as that,' Len shouted, and kicked the dog's dish over the threshold on his way out to sulk in the woodshed.

Miss Taylor, being at work in the afternoon, could not attend the MU. But she was well enough aware of her position in the village to realize she was on dangerous ground if she supported the WI. Nevertheless, the WI was recognized as educational, and it did meet in her school. Indeed, it was she, in unlikely partnership with May Quinton, who had succeeded in establishing a branch of the WI in the village. She had been its first president, with May as her secretary, and it was only very recently that she had insisted on standing down in favour of Mrs Jeffs so that true democracy should be seen to be at work. She solved the problem of her partiality neatly by insisting that Miss Nellie abjure the WI completely, and join the MU.

Nellie had protested. 'But I'm not a mother, Kathleen,' she had said. 'And it's plain now I'm never going to be one. But I am a woman. I don't want to waste an afternoon a month praying for the sanctity of other women's marriages, and being polite to the Vicar. You know what I think about *him*!'

Kathleen was adamant. 'Charity Wells belongs,' she said,

'and she attends the meetings regularly. She's quite as old as I am, and unmarried. Surely what is good enough for her is good enough for you? Besides, I wish you to go, for my sake.'

Nellie was used to obliging her sister, and could, indeed, see the reasoning; but she did object to Charity Wells being held up as an example to her. That lady was a spinster of some means, who lived in Lilac Cottage and played the grand lady whenever opportunity arose.

'Charity Wells?' Miss Nellie snorted. 'She'd join a society for knitting combinations for gorillas if she thought the Vicar would be there!'

The Vicar was unmarried also. Miss Nellie said it was because all women had more sense than consider him as a husband; but there was no doubt that Charity had a different opinion. She baked her specialities on the morning of the second Tuesday, and never handed them in to the Enrolling Member on arrival, as the others did. She manoeuvred herself into a chair next to the Vicar, and produced her 'refreshments' at the appropriate moment.

'Oh, I am so sorry!' she would say in her throaty voice, 'I quite forgot my little contribution! But I know the dear Vicar likes my Viennese fancies. We'll just leave them within his reach, shall we? Do help yourself, Vicar.'

There was also much ribald amusement at her expense. Report had it that once when she was ill the Vicar had called to see her, and she had tried to drag him into bed with her. She had been 'a bit queer in the head' about that time.

'Well, it's nature, at her age, don't you see,' said George Willis sagely. 'They say that what you never 'ev, you never miss—but Charity does. Tha's what's her trouble.'

The rumour could not be substantiated, of course; but the thought of such an incident was not to be disposed of without the last bit of interest being squeezed from it.

'It 'minds me o' a chap as used to work wi' me on't farm when I were a youngster,' Timmy said in The Star. ' 'E goes t't boss one day an' says 'e wants to leave work early-like in t'afternoon, 'cos 'e were goin' to take 'is sweetheart black-berryin'. When he come t' work next morning, t'boss says, "Nice day tha 'ad yest'day for thi' outin', Jack! Did thi' get what thi' wanted?"

' "Aye, a' did that," Jack says, "an a couple o' pound o' blackberries in t't bargain!" '

It was at the Mothers' Union meeting that the blow fell on Charity Wells. The Vicar had been late in arriving, and she had not been able to keep a vacant chair next to her. The Enrolling Member had fussed about, looking very important, and had actually been heard to say to the tea hostess for the afternoon that she wished to keep a chair next to her for the Vicar when he came. When at last he took his seat, he wore an air of embarrassment quite foreign to him, and seemed a good deal less interested than usual in the refreshments. Then the Enrolling Member stood up, and clapped her hands for silence.

'Dear members,' she said. 'I have some sad news for you, and some glad ones to follow it. We are to lose our dear Vicar very soon.' (Murmurs all round, quite inaudible. Stunned silence on the part of Miss Wells.) The Enrolling Member, after suitable pause, enlarged on her theme. 'We must not grudge him to his lucky new parish, which is much larger than ours, and much more compact, so that he will be in charge of one congregation only. But we shall all miss him dreadfully, as I am sure you will agree. And now I have his permission to tell you his other piece of news, which will make everyone of you rejoice with him. He is to be married! The lucky lady, whom he has known since childhood, is the daughter of the bishop of the new diocese in which he will be working.'

The ladies, it seemed, were struck dumb, and could find no words to express their prescribed joy. When they had at last recovered from the shock of surprise and incredulity, they began to murmur their awkward congratulations and other comments aloud.

Charity Wells had gone very white, and then very red, and had had difficulty in restraining tears; yet it was her voice that was heard above the others, saying huskily: 'Oh, the dear Vicar! How sweet! It really is too romantic!'

Her thoughts had already flown to the possibility of his replacement. The Enrolling Member was talking again, saying that the Vicar had asked to be excused now, as he had much to do. So he left, though not before sampling the goodies pressed on him from all sides.

When he had gone, they had turned their thoughts to the problem of raising money for a suitable gift, and to a suitable way of presenting it.

'The village as a whole will be making a parting gift to the Vicar,' the Enrolling Member was saying; 'and of course the church congregation will do so, as well. But under the circumstances of his marriage, we of the Mothers' Union must make a special effort. Perhaps we can have it ready to present at our next meeting.'

Much discussion swept backwards and forwards with regard to the nature of the gift, which in turn depended on the amount of money to be collected. (Some ladies had already worked out that they would be asked to contribute at least three times.) Suggestions ranged from an illuminated address (Charity) to a cookery book (Miss Nellie); but the discussion petered out in favour of one with regard to the place and time of the presentation.

In the end, though both the EM and Miss Wells were against it (the EM because she feared having to organize it, Charity because it was so unashamedly bucolic), it was decided to put forward their annual social, in the hope that the Vicar and his intended could both be in attendance at it.

Buzzing with suppressed excitement, the meeting then broke up to disseminate the extraordinary news. Charity took her plate of Viennese fancies back home again, with a hollow place in her heart, the place which until today had been filled with dogged hope. How had she failed? While he had remained a confirmed bachelor, there was no sting in his rebuttal of her charms; but for him to succumb after all this

81

time to the wiles of another—the thought to her was as cold as charity indeed.

Socials took place during the winter, and were usually quite enjoyable occasions. No one expected The Family, The (Priory) School, or Campion's Hall to have any part of them; they were recognized as truly village affairs. On the other hand, it was almost obligatory on the farmers and their wives to attend, or at least to be represented by members of their family. Other people went or not, according to their personal preference, but on the whole these gatherings displayed a fair cross-section of the community.

Once going, such all-in occasions practically ran themselves; but they had to be set going, and songs, games, sketches and so on organized in advance. This was the point of some difference in the quality of the good time had by all; some people had the gift of entertaining others, and some had not.

The annual MU social was not quite such a spontaneous affair as the others. People went to it who did not normally patronize the other village hops, and the proceedings had a much more elevated tone. Consequently, they were often heavy occasions that fell rather flat for want of the young set's vitality, and the spontaneity offered by the likes of Reggie Pettigrew.

There was much to-ing and fro-ing among the members of the MU about the organization of their social. The Enrolling Member and Charity Wells were definitely at loggerheads with Miss Nellie about it. Charity had insisted that as the Vicar, and probably his intended, were to be present, the whole tone of the evening must be kept high. She had, she said, in the past trained many choirs, and would willingly train the members of their branch to sing some 'good' songs— good, muscially, that is. She also offered the services of her great friend, who was a violinist. Then perhaps the EM herself would do an uplifting monologue, and they could ask Gladys to sing (Gladys was one of the pre-WI unmarrieds to join the MU, chapel-oriented though she was).

Miss Nellie was half-hearted about the whole business, anyway, but was inured by years of practice to doing her bit without protest; but she argued that you couldn't mix 'culture' with a village social, and that if you wanted to give a high-class concert you should announce it as such. In the end, they struck a compromise. If Miss Nellie would make herself responsible for the games and dancing, with a few of the expected bits of entertainment, they would produce an interlude, so to speak, to surround the speeches and the actual presentation. Miss Nellie had at first demurred; but after a minute's thought, during which a close observer might have detected a wicked little twinkle in her eye, she consented on condition she could ask 'others' to help her. Charity and the EM both agreed, abstractedly. Each was planning one-upmanship on the other for the only part of the affair that to them was worth bothering about. Miss Nellie left them to their cogitations, and set off purposefully to enlist May Quinton and Nurse Hardy. She would certainly do her best to get the Vicar's marriage off to a sanctified start. A large question mark hung over the sanctity of May's marriage, while Nurse Hardy was nothing if not robust in her approach to the life she saw 'in the raw'. She was full of vitality herself, and in the next village, where she lived, she had been instrumental in setting up a popular concert party. Miss Nellie could not help feeling that she would provide a perfect antidote to Charity Wells's choir's offering of 'good' music. She began to look forward to the presentation social for quite the wrong reasons, at least as far as the Mothers' Union was concerned.

6 Life's uncertain, but death sure

The news struck the village like an earth tremor, stunning it into frightened silence for an hour or two before feeling returned and expressed itself in voluble talk. The Duke was dead. He had died sitting in his favourite chair at The Lodge, after coming in from a tramp round The Priory grounds with his dog. His housekeeper reported that he 'had not been himself' for a day or two previously, and had complained a great deal of cold, though other people had remarked how muggy it was for the time of the year. She had sent for Dr Leathers at once, but he had been too late.

'I'm sure my 'eads numb,' Sally Woods had said to May Quinton. 'My 'ead's real numb. Ain't your 'ead numb, Mis' Quinton?'

May could not honestly say that it was, but she knew what Sally meant. It was difficult to imagine The Lodge without its hearty occupant, or the village 'topped' like a thistle under a billhook. If people ever had looked into the future to estimate the effect the death of the present Duke would have on them, they had never given utterance to their thoughts. He was only just over seventy, and seemed to be as tough as nails. There was no need to meet trouble before it arrived. The trouble that might have been foreseen was that the Duke's death would occasion a break with The Family, for there was no heir apparent on the spot. The Duke had had two sons. The older had been killed, unmarried, in the war. The second, a bit of a young rake, had been in the USA when war broke out, but had come home at once, bringing with him a young American wife, already pregnant. She had disliked wartime England and the countryside, hated the Priory as a home, and loathed her father-in-law. Indeed, there was no love lost between them at all, for he regarded her in every way as the complete antithesis of what a member of the English aristocracy should be. He had not at first considered her as a future duchess, because at that time his heir was still alive and well. When he was killed, the Duke had to face up to reality. His less satisfactory son must now inherit. The lady began to give herself airs as the future duchess and to talk openly about what she would do to make 'this old barn of a place' fit to live in. But before a second child was born, the war claimed the second of the Duke's sons, too. If that baby should be a boy, he would be heir to the title. If it should be another girl, then the title would go to an impoverished cousin of doubtful character. Thank God the estate was not entailed.

The child was a boy; but before he was old enough to toddle, his mother had a flaming row with the Duke, and carried her son with her back to America.

There were few in the village or around it that were directly affected by the Duke's death in material ways, but even fewer who did not feel in some way depleted by it.

Marston, the agent, the gamekeepers and grooms, the house-keeper and maids, the gardener and the odd-job man felt some sense of insecurity, but it was the nature of such jobs that they went with the property. Until it was known how the Duke had disposed of his private fortune, they could only speculate. If the new young duke did return, he would most likely keep them on because they knew the place, and he didn't. If The Lodge and the estate were sold, the same could very well apply, but in any case it was bound to be years before it was all settled up. The lease of The Priory to the school had been for ninety-nine years, of which only eight or nine had run. There was no urgency in that quarter; nevertheless, the flag was run up to half-mast, and the school mourned a good friend and neighbour, who could be counted on to understand the public school way of life.

Reg Pettigrew was affected more than most. He had got on well with the Duke on the few occasions when they had met by chance, and had found him easy to talk to, with views on many things that matched Reggie's own; he had considered the Duke a fair, if somewhat exacting landlord, and the farmer knew quite well that such concessions as had been granted him were of the Duke's rather than the agent's doing. His tenancy was safe enough for the moment, even if the estate was sold eventually. It was the immediate future that bothered Reggie, whose commonsense told him that for the next few months, at any rate, all affairs concerning the land would be in Marston's hands. Under the circumstances, this was not too rosy a prospect.

But for the moment, it was the fact of death itself that was concerning everyone.

> *The glories of our blood and state*
> *Are shadows, not substantial things.*
> *There is no armour against Fate.*
> *Death lays his icy hand on kings.*

The Professor quoted the verse sadly. And for once his sister got the gist of his quotation, and capped it neatly by saying tersely, 'Young men may die; old men must,' with a look that spoke her thoughts as plainly as if she had uttered them. The Professor and the Duke were very much of an age.

Bert Stobbs had enough sense to conceal his satisfaction at 'the deemise of a haristocrat' from everyone but May and Aunt Mabel.

'That's one less for the rest of us to keep,' he said. 'His title or his money couldn't make him nothing only an ordinary yuman being, like the rest of us, as had to go when his time come.' Bert, too, felt disposed to quote, thinking darkly on his own wrongs. 'God don't pay his debts wi' money,' he said.

Mrs Bluett went gleaning details from her sister's oldest daughter, who was a maid at The Lodge. She took her bag of titbits down to the shop, which was rarely empty for more than five minutes on the day after the news broke.

Miss Nellie had gone to buy stamps, and had stopped to chat with May until joined by Mrs Watson.

'Dearie me O,' said Mrs Watson, 'whoever would have thought it! We shall have a grand funeral, I'll be bound! When his father died, men from the estate pulled the cart with the coffin on all the way from The Priory to the church. An' the young duke—that's this one as has just died—he had to 'old 'is mother up when they come to putting the coffin in the vault. I thought she were going to faint right away, dearie me O, that I did!'

Aunt Mabel, fiddling with her hearing aid (her earphone, she always called it), nodded to substantiate Mrs Watson's account.

'They just couldn't pacify her no-how,' Aunt Mabel said. 'Cried enough tears to bath a cow in.'

Miss Nellie caught May's eye, and was forced to search her handbag for a handkerchief. May sought to head Mrs Watson and Aunt Mabel off from the threatened contest of memory.

'He had been ill, had he? I hadn't heard of him being laid up.'

'Been ailing for about two days,' yelled Mrs Bluett, 'so my sister's Junie says. She went to make the old feiler's fire up, and she says he told 'er to keep all the winders shut, 'cos 'e were so cold. But the housekeeper ordered her to open 'em all again. "He must 'av air," she says, "whether 'e wants it or not. Ventilation's better than cure, that's my motter," she says. Then when Junie opened 'em, the duke got up and shut 'em, and roared at Junie so loud she darsn't go near 'em no more. Never did see 'im no more alive, after that.'

'Do you know what he died of?' asked Miss Nellie. Mrs

Bluett took the centre of the stage, so that all might hear, including Aunt Mabel.

'Junie said as it said some word like "signcope" on the death cerstificate. But the housekeeper told our Junie as that were just the doctor's way o' keeping folks guessing. She said 'e had told her what it meant. You, see, 'is 'eart 'ad broke up in to little bits, an' were floatin' about in 'is blood. Then one o' these bits touched 'is brain, an' that surrendered 'im. It's a bad job, I'm sure.'

'They do say as 'e wanted to be cremated. But dearie me O, how are you to know the truth when you hear it?'

Truth nowhere shows more faces than it does in a village. By nightfall there were four different versions of the truth concerning the projected funeral rites, and three, all contradictory, about the new young duke's whereabouts and future plans.

Talk at The Star barely left the subject. Geoff Pettigrew had come over to see Reggie as soon as he had heard the news, and the two brothers, with Roddy in attendance, had slipped out of Stavesacre kitchen to the comparative peace of Charlie's fireside.

Roddy, who was now twenty, was not a frequent visitor to The Star, because he owned a motorbike and liked to take his refreshment a bit farther afield than the pub in his own village. He was already well known all round the district as a likeable young madcap. No one ever knew what he was going to get up to next. But he was so handsome and his tricks were usually so funny that he was regarded with great affection by most people, male and female alike.

Tonight, as he followed his father and uncle up to the bar, he had his jacket buttoned up as far as it would go, and a thick scarf wound round his throat, with the ends tucked into the neck of the jacket, forming a bulge on his chest that he occasionally patted. Though he removed his leather helmet and motorcyclist's goggles, he left the scarf undisturbed. They took their drinks and half-turned to join in the conversation. George Willis had the floor.

'I knowed as there were going to be a death here afore long,' he was saying. 'When I were doing the yardwork last week, there were a grut ol' barn owl flying so low over the village as you couldn't mistake what it meant. It sailed slow like over my 'ead, I could nearly a' touched it. It were saying "Who? Who?" all the while, and I says to myself, "Yer needn't kick up a bloody row like that there, 'cos you know very well who, without askin'." I watched to see where it 'ould settle, but it went out o' sight. Now I come to think about it, it did go off Priory way.'

'Do you really believe in such omens, then?' Charlie asked. (Charlie wanted to believe with all his heart; but so far he'd never even had a whiff of an omen, let alone a glimpse of a ghost.)

'You can't go agin 'em,' George said, 'onct you know what they mean. When my ol' father died, we 'ad a warnin' as everybody could understand. You know, 'e were a bit of a clock man—used to do clocks up for folks. Ah, he loved clocks, my ol' dad did. He'd buy 'em in sales, an' then do 'em up so's they'd go and keep good time. Most likely then 'e didn't want to part with 'em, so they'd stand all uvver the 'ouse. There were one ol' grandfather clock 'as 'ad belonged to my grandad, an' about ten others, timepieces of all sorts. Me and mother set 'eving our tea, and father called out from his bedroom next to us, "What's the time?" Then I see as mother 'ad brought all the clocks out o' the bedroom, like they mostly did then when anybody were bad abed. She looked up at the ol' grandfather, an' I see 'er go white. It had stopped at twenty-five minutes past four. Then she looked at the one on the mantelpiece but that had stopped an' all—at twenty-five minutes past four. An' so 'ad every other bloody clock in the 'ouse! We knowed then as 'e wouldn't last above another twenty-four hours at the most. An it's as true as I set 'ere, he died in the early hours o' the next mornin' at twenty-five minutes past four.'

Roddy (and indeed all the Pettigrew family) was listening avidly; but Roddy looked a bit sceptical, all the same.

'How did you know what time he died, if all the clocks in the house had stopped?' he asked.

'We 'eard the church clock strike the half just as he were drawin' 'is last breath,' said George, nothing perturbed. 'An' it's allus been atween five and ten minutes fast.'

Charlie wanted to ask if and when all the clocks had last been wound up; but on the whole he thought better of it. George might take another pointed question as a slur on his veracity, and whatever the real truth was, there was no doubt that he believed the version he was telling.

Roddy lifted his mug to drink, resting the hard bottom rim of it against the bulge on his chest. A long-drawn-out muffled mew came from the direction of the bar. After the third or fourth mew, George Willis said, 'I didn't know as you 'ad a cat, Charlie. 'Ow long have you 'ad it?'

Charlie looked all round the bar, puzzled. 'I ain't got no cat,' he said. 'Dolly can't abide 'em.'

'Well, sounds as if one's got in, some'ow,' George said. 'Is it under the floorboards?'

'That it ain't,' said Charlie, a bit nettled. 'How would a cat get under this tiled floor? The floor's been here about more'n three hundred year.'

George had his head on one side, listening. 'So's that cat, I shouldn't wonder,' he said. 'When anything like this 'ere death 'appens, it sets off all sorts o' queer things. Stands to reason a place as old as this 'ere must be 'aunted. You're quite like got a cat 'aunt as wants to tell you som'at.'

Roddy, ignoring the continued plaintive mewing, caught his father's eye, and grinned. Then he said, 'That reminds me—I wanted to ask you something. Roly says one o' the rules at the school is that nobody can keep pets of any kind, not even the masters who live in the grounds—on account o' the pheasants. But when I were coming home the night before last, on my motorbike, the lights picked out something on the road in front o' me, just before I got to The Priory gates. I slowed up 'cos I thought at first it was some of our calves got out from the

90

Home Cluss. But it turned out to be a couple of big dogs—hounds, I'd say, running side by side for all the world as if they were in leash, though there was nobody with 'em. When they got to The Priory gates, they turned in and kept going up towards the house. I never thought no more about 'em, till now.'

Charlie looked distinctly uneasy, and when George opened his mouth to speak, Charlie scowled at him, to shut him up. Then he said to Roddy, 'I reckon the beer at The Rising Sun must be a lot stronger than mine, to make you see such things. As far as I know, there ain't no black dogs down yonder. As you say, it's one o' the rules.'

There was another prolonged wail of cat-like noise. 'Where can that dratted cat be, I wonder,' Charlie said, glad of the excuse to change the subject.

Roddy was preparing to leave. 'I'm going down to The Rising Sun now,' he said to his father and uncle. 'My passenger is gettin' impatient.'

He unwound the scarf from his neck, and opened his jacket. He was wearing a hand-knitted woollen pullover with a V-neck, and tight ribbing at the waist. From above the point of the V, the head of a half-grown cat protruded, the rest of it lodged against his diaphragm and held in place by the wool.

'All right, Tittles,' he said, stroking the cat's ears, and immediately producing a purr. 'You'll ride warmer there tonight than in my coat pocket.' He settled the kitten again, and replaced his scarf.

'Well, as I go to school,' said George Willis. 'I ain't never seen the like o' that afore!'

'Nor me neither,' said Charlie. 'I'll give you cat 'aunts!' Roddy put on his hat and goggles, and left them to it.

' 'E is a one,' said George. 'You never know what 'e'll be up to next! Does 'e take that bloody cat to The Rising Sun, really?'

Reggie nodded. 'It goes everywhere with him,' he said. 'He's trained it since before it got its eyes open. It'll ride in his pocket with its head hanging out, or stuck up his jumper, or even round his neck—anywhere he puts it, it'll stop.'

91

'I say, though—what did you make o' the tale about the hounds?' Charlie answered slowly. 'George 'ere knows what it were he saw,' he said, 'but The Family don't like it talked about, and it's so long now since anybody see 'em that I reckon we'd all nearly forgot. It's the sign The Family allus get when there's going to be a death in it. The funny thing is, though, that it's other folk who see 'em. An' there can be two folks walking along together, an' one'll see 'em but the other won't. What's queer about young Roddy seein' 'em is that he says they looked as if they were in leash, but there was nobody with 'em. The last to see 'em, just before Lord Francis was killed, said there was a monk trotting along behind 'em. And that's what the legend says. They reckon that in olden times when the monks lived up at The Priory, one of the young 'uns used to let himself out o' nights and visit some gal up in the village. He had this pair o' hounds and used to take them with him to give 'em a run, and no doubt for his own protection as well. But they found him trying to get in, one night in winter. The Prior at that time were a real old devil, they say. He had the poor young man flogged, and then as a penance he ordered him to stand out all night with bare feet and nothing on only his shirt. The legend goes that it was the coldest night they'd ever had. He was alive in the morning, but before the week was out he'd died. Caught pneumonia, I don't doubt!

'Now they reckon the monk haunts The Priory, 'cos that's where it all happened, and where he were buried, in the wall of a new bit that the monks happened to be building at the time. Ever so many folks has seen him, wandering about The Priory—though I ain't heard of it happening since the school took over. But when there's going to be a death, he's seen in the grounds with his hounds on a leash!'

(Charlie enjoyed the telling of that. He also enjoyed the rapt attention of his audience, the Pettigrew brothers. There were not many who would have listened so long without laughing, or contradicting his version of it, or something. But the few who did know of the legend were getting fewer. The duke had been afraid it would put a spoke in the wheels of his plan to turn The Priory back into a seat of learning, and had done his best to suppress it.)

George had listened intently, too, though he had heard it all many times before. He felt that Roddy's seeing of the dogs completely vindicated his own stories from any trace of falsehood. Besides, he was concerned with the whys and wherefores of the recent apparition.

'Night afore last—that'd be the night afore he died. That fits! But why didn't he see the monk, I wonder? An' why should it be a stranger-like, one as didn't know the tale, as it appeared to? I ha'n't heard as none o' the real old village folk see'd it. Why should young Roddy?'

He seemed a bit put out, as if a privilege belonging to the indigenous population had been usurped. It was Geoff Pettigrew who answered, a bit reluctantly, perhaps, but gravely and in serious vein.

'Well—it isn't everyone as can see. The few who do are them with the gift of seeing. I reckon Roddy's got it—like me. All our family have got it, on'y some more than others. I've got it specially, 'cos I were born on the stroke o' midnight. So were Roddy. We've never told him about that, 'cos we didn't want him to be scared all his life by it if there were no need—specially as we'd all left our own home district. We thought it might have died out. Reg, here—he's never really seen nothing for certain, though he reckons there's queer things happen up at Stavesacre. On'y for the Lord's sake, don't say nothing so that Reggie's wife gets to hear! But Reg, you see, wasn't born at midnight. I was—an' I could tell you some tales!'

It was only on the way back to Stavesacre that Reg remembered again what he had had in mind to ask. He had meant to ask Charlie or George what they could tell him about 'the hanging tree' on his land. Geoff said he'd never heard of it, but didn't propose to put his power of seeing to the test if he could help it. Reg said he hoped Roddy wouldn't be tempted to

93

experiment—he couldn't make up his mind whether it would be safer to warn the boy, or not. Geoff thought not; he was well aware that nothing would induce Gwen to stop at Stavesacre if reports of it being haunted reached her.

'But you know as it's haunted, don't you?' Geoff asked, as they strolled home.

'I don't *know*,' Reg replied. 'But I've got a pretty good idea.'

'Where do you reckon?'

'Well—I can *feel* something queer, as makes the hair on my arms stand up, some nights on the front staircase—it's as if all sorts o' folks I can't see are bumping up against me, and I have a job to get through 'em. But they can't be ordinary folks, 'cos none of 'em come up to my waist—well, only thereabouts! It's my legs and thighs they run into.'

'Ah, that's it,' said Geoff.

'What do you mean, that's it?' said Reg, stopping in the middle of the road. 'Do you mean that you've felt 'em, an' all?'

Geoff shook his head. He was sweating, and wiped his forehead with a large handkerchief before pulling his trilby hat firmly down again.

'No,' he said, 'I can't say as I've ever *felt* 'em, but I've heard 'em, and what you say bears out what I've heard. It scares me more'n anything else I've ever seen. Two or three times, on them stairs, I've 'eard laughing all round me—happy laughing, merry-like—like a whole gang o' children playing. I thought the first time that it was some sort of echo from where your kids were at play, only there were a lot too many voices, all younger than Roly, but older than Angie. Now you say you can feel 'em—just about the right size. Children! I wonder what happened to 'em, Reggie!'

'For God's sake don't tell nobody else,' said Reg. 'Things are bound to be bad enough wi' Marston and his gang for a bit, now. I don't want no more complications wi' Gwen. She wouldn't stop another minute if she ever found out.'

They walked home in serious silence.

7 . . . and women must weep

The funeral had been arranged. The agent and the family lawyer, between them, had followed all customary precedents. His Grace would not be cremated, but laid to rest with his forebears in the vault on the side of the churchyard. He would travel on his last journey on one of Reggie Pettigrew's four-wheeled wagons, pulled by two black, beplumed carthorses—one from Stavesacre, one from Pellmell. The bearers would be six men of equal height chosen from his tenants and workforce, Reg Pettigrew among them, though it was a task he detested. After the nearest relatives would come the rest of his kin, among them representing all ranks of the British aristocracy. Next friends and acquaintances, including doctors, lawyers, clerks and the like. Then the masters and the boys of the Upper School (excluding Monty Price and the choir, who would be in church); following them would be representatives of all the many bodies and institutions the Duke had supported during the last few years, from Old Comrades to Boy Scouts, from The Old Boys' Association to the Farmers' Union local branch. Last, all the employees of the estate, at The Lodge and on the tenant farms.

The agent had wished to lay His Grace's ducal robes over the coffin, and stand his coronet upon it. The lawyer was able

95

to squash the notion flat by producing strict instructions in the Duke's own hand. The coffin was to lie unadorned on the wagon, except for a bunch of wild flowers gathered by school-children from the estate. The Duke, like Charlie, had been a real romantic under his bluff exterior.

Miss Taylor took the children to gather the flowers, and had enough sense to arrange them into a simple sheaf. The farmers gathered dark branches of pine and yew to make a fragrant bed for the coffin, and intertwined them with long, graceful trails of glistening ivy.

The procession would be a long one, and the progress slow; it had to pass through the village as far as the church, and it was tacitly understood that those who were not following would line the route from the village outskirts to the church yard gate. The lower school of The Priory would stand shoulder to shoulder on the road outside the church, and village school-children from the gate to the church door. All must be suitably clothed in dark garments, and their teachers likewise.

For a village funeral, no one but the mourners, which included all who wished 'to pay their last respects', would have been seen. The route by which the sad cortège went from cottage to church would have been left clear of traffic, blinds drawn in every dwelling en route, and children kept in school till all was over. Grief would be accorded respectful privacy; and if some of the housebound lifted the corner of the blind as the hearse passed, it was only to take farewell of a neighbour or drop a tear in sympathy with the bereaved.

This was different; the Duke was a public man, and his funeral had to be as public as possible, to match his status when living.

From far and wide, relatives and friends descended on the village, as people of both sexes and all ages returned 'home' for the day, some to show their respects, and some to satisfy curiosity.

May Quinton was to have a visitor—or to put it more truthfully, Aunt Mabel was. May had had a call on the post office telephone, from the daughter of one of Aunt Mabel's contemporaries who had left the village many years ago. She had got it into her head that she wanted to see the Duke's funeral, and pay her last respects. After all, she had been under-nursemaid at The Priory when the Duke was born, and if she was now eighty-four, she was still spry and lively. Aunt Mabel had often invited her to 'stop a few days' with her. Could she come so as to be there on the day?

May was cagey on the telephone, and promised to let the daughter know. Aunt Mabel, in her early eighties, was quite unpredictable in a matter of this nature. If May had agreed, Aunt Mabel would probably have declared that she never could abide so-and-so, and wouldn't have her across the threshold. On the other hand, if May put the least obstacle in the way of the visit, Aunt Mabel would have taken umbrage immediately, asking pointedly whose house it was, and why everybody wanted to deny her the only pleasure she now had.

May might have said that one old lady (to say nothing of a difficult uncle, two children, a shop and post office) was enough for her to cope with, but she forebore. As it turned out, Aunt Mabel was disposed, at the moment, to a mood of lachrymose nostalgia.

She couldn't think of anything nicer than to see Ruth, and talk over old times. May was to arrange the visit with all speed, in case the Lord should take one or the other of them before they could meet again. Aunt Mabel spent the intervening days recalling the past to anybody who would listen. The heroine of her reminiscences was rarely Ruth, though the villain was undoubtedly Johnno, Ruth's wayward husband. Uncle Bert was sick of the sound of Ruth long before she arrived, especially when he learned that she had actually dandled the dead aristocrat on her knee when he was a baby.

'Slavery, that's what it used to be! Nothing but slavery, for one yuman being to be in service to another, like that.'

'It's all done now, anyway,' he declared with satisfaction. 'There won't be any more half-starved little girls lugging great

97

overfed babies about for five pounds a year. Them as bring 'em into the world 'll have to look after 'em themselves, from now on.'

Aunt Mabel never could resist such provocation from her brother-in-law. If he hadn't voiced such sentiments, she quite likely would have done; but nobody ever got the better of her in argument. Even if she beat her opponent into submission, the verbal contest was not brought to a close.

'Well, that's what I say,' she would declare, looking balefully through her thick lenses at the loser, and with a wrestler's skill she would suddenly re-open the contest by somersaulting smartly (metaphorically speaking, of course) till she brought herself up in the other corner, facing the opposite way. The extraordinary thing was that her exasperated opponent would without fail defend himself, and find himself also on the opposite side from which he'd started. Bert, certainly, was no match for her. He would eventually retire from the fray looking like a fighting cock that had been well feathered, and say to May, under his breath, 'Ignorant, that's all I can say! It's all village ignorance. It makes you wonder, don't it?'

'I'm no more ignorant than you are, Bert Stobbs. I know what I know! An' there's one thing I know, and that is that nobody like the Duke or Lord Wimperris would be so ignorant as to call folks names behind their backs! You didn't think I should 'ear you, did you? You just mind what you lay your tongue to! I don't want no labour folks in my 'ouse.'

Aunt Mabel invariably picked up the gist of anything she was not supposed to hear, especially if Bert was talking politics. It made no difference that she was as innocent of political understanding as a sow is of sidepockets. She was a radical Liberal in theory, and a dyed-in-the-wool Conservative in practice. To have been given a vote pleased her; to use it would be beneath her dignity.

But nostalgia was the strongest emotion in the few days before Ruth arrived. Aunt Mabel sat in her great chair, overflowing in every direction, with her earphone at the ready, and mused on better days gone by. Every now and then she would break into song—or at least, into hymn—with as much throat-clearing as if she were about to deliver an operatic aria, before producing an untuneful, husky little rendering of

> *Till we mee-ee-eet, till we mee-eet,*
> *Till we meet, at Jee-ees-you-ous feet,*
> *Till we mee-ee-eet, till we mee-eet,*
> *God be with you till we meet again.*

Sankey and Moody had not worked in vain among rural people with a natural ear for music.

May borrowed an old pony and buggy from Dindle, and drove down to the nearest railway halt, about a mile and a half away, to pick Ruth up from the train, only with great difficulty dissuading Aunt Mabel from attempting the journey. There were times when she flatly refused to acknowledge her eighty-plus years, her eighteen-stone-plus weight, and her knees that failed to hold her up for more than a few steps. She had no compunction about laying all these disabilities directly at the door of whomever it was that was so disobligingly thwarting her desires. She was far more autocratic than ever the Duke had been. In the event, she sulked at home until May delivered the wisp that Ruth had become into her massive, outstretched arms.

'Cripes!' said May to the old pony, as she turned his head towards Dindle again. 'What have I let us all in for!'

The two old ladies could not have been more unlike each other to look at. Aunt Mabel in weight and size would have made three of Ruth Pollington. Aunt Mabel's snow-white hair was plentiful and long. May had to brush and comb it every morning, plait it, and coil it up into a bun. The centre parting, that had been in the same place for eighty years, had widened to a broad track from which wings of white hair were swept back and up round a broad plump face of still unblemished 'peaches and cream' complexion. Her eyes were golden brown, flecked with red when she lost her temper, which was by no means a rare occurrence. Ruth's face was tiny, clean-cut like a cameo, with a tiny pointed chin, high cheekbones and a sharp pointed nose. Her eyes were still dark blue, and darted from side to side like a bird caught in a room. Her hair had always been naturally curly, but never long or luxuriant. The modern short style of bobbing had suited her. She wore her white hair cropped short enough to curl all over her head. Her hands and feet, both worn and knobbled with hard work, were hardly bigger than those of a child, and when she sat on a chair, her short little legs dangled an inch or two from the floor.

There, however, with the physical disparities, the differences between them ended. In character, they were much alike—equally purposeful to the point of stubbornness, domineering when opportunity arose, always garrulous, often critical, and defensive or compliant in turn, as *amour propre* demanded.

They talked, unbridled, for six hours without pause, except for sudden, breath-holding trips 'round the back', Ruth trotting off under her own steam, but Aunt Mabel having to be taken by May, whatever that lady might happen to be engaged in. When the imperious summons rang out, it was like a call to action stations in time of battle for the rest of the family. Even Uncle Bert, when present, was commanded to open the door, the children to pick up the walkingsticks, and the cat sent scuttling out of the way.

There was no discreet modesty possible when Aunt Mabel felt the call, though she herself always wore an extraordinary, lop-sided expression when she came back, as if to convince everybody that she had merely been stargazing or communing with the Almighty.

The two old friends, who were also old adversaries on many issues, sat one each side of the fire, for the weather was bitter with the first frosts of winter. They held their hands to the blaze in concert, and rubbed their rheumaticky knees in chorus. After the first flush of exploration as to how each stood, physically and with regard to ailments, in comparison with the other, their talk drifted away into the doings of their respective families, and then to mutual acquaintances, which of course included everybody connected with the village over a span of eighty years. As May said before bedtime on their first evening together, there wasn't a single person left with reputation intact or scutcheon unsmirched. They investigated every pedigree, through sire and dam, throughout three and four generations, and the air was thick with the rattle of skeletal bones dragged mercilessly from cupboards where they had long been concealed. The advantage Aunt Mabel had on account of having lived so long in the village was countered by Ruth's intimate knowledge of the goings on up at The Priory in the days of 'the old duke' in Victorian times, when royalty often visited there for weekend parties.

'Ugh! I couldn't abear the Prince of Wales,' Ruth said. 'He were getting on to be an old man then, but if 'e happened to meet you, he'd look at you as if he were strippin' the clo'e's right off you, and you'd feel as if you were stan'in' there naked in your shift. Some o' the gals didn't used to care—they used to quarrel about which one of 'em would take his mornin' tea. You see, there'd very often be a gold sovereign for the one who did—only it wasn't for taking his tea, you understand.'

Aunt Mabel's eyes lit up. 'Did you ever—?'

'No, that I never did! I were only fourteen, and my Mam 'ad drilled it into me before I left 'ome that she didn't want none of her gals coming home with five pounds in her hand and six pounds in her belly! Kept myself to myself, I did, till I started going out with Johnno. No gal weren't safe with him five minutes.

'I should never have married him if it hadn't been for my Mam being so strict with us. When I knowed as I were going to have a child, I darn't go home. I kep' it a secret until after we were married. But it's as true as I set 'ere, the day I went to church to marry Johnno, I stood in the doorway an' prayed as God would strike me dead, or let the church fall on me, afore I got up to the altar. I knowed as I'd let myself in for worry and trouble, and misery, but I didn't know the half, then! Not the half! If I had done, I'd have jumped in the river afore I'd have gone through with it. I'm often thought I should ha' been a lot better off with a few gold sovereigns an' me year's wages in my 'and! Ah, I made my bed all right, and I had to lay on it, for nigh on sixty year!'

Ruth was not disposed to be sorry for herself now—she was merely angry in retrospect for the unkind trick Fate had played on her, Aunt Mabel was the one who was near to tears.

'Ah, you did have a time, an' no mistake. If ever a gal had to set a hard heart against hard sorrow, it were you. All that hussle o' children, an' Johnno so drunk as he couldn't work three days out o' every four. But I must say he were a handsome man—handsome as a picture when he were dressed up.'

' 'Andsome is as 'andsome does,' snapped Ruth. 'Once he'd took advantage o' me one Sunday night up in Longacre, I knowed as I'd sold my soul to the devil in disguise. 'Cos that's what 'e were—the devil hisself, I reckon. But with the Lord's 'elp, I got through. An' I outlived 'im!'

She rocked herself backwards and forwards as memory after memory flooded in upon her; but May, taking her a cup of cocoa to go to bed on, noted a triumphant twinkle in her eye, and wondered on the cause of it. Uncle Bert, coming in from a visit to his crony, put an end for the moment to further reminiscences.

'What time's the balloon going up tomorrow?' he asked.

'If you mean the funeral, I'll thank you to say so,' snapped Aunt Mabel. 'Though what concern it is of yours, I can't think. You don't mean to pay no last respec's, that I do know!'

'No fear! You won't find me kow-towing to no ol' bag o' bones whosever they are. I've 'elped to put too many in their boxes. But I shall be 'ere to see the last of 'im, an' good riddance. It'll give me real pleasure to see that ol' whoresbud goin' on 'is last journey. 'Appy day! 'Appy day! The day they took—the Duke away,' he parodied.

'O! you blastpheemious old humbug!' gasped Aunt Mabel. 'Bad'll become o' you, mark my words!'

May got them to bed at last, as excited as children on Christmas Eve, including Uncle Bert. She wondered at his apparent jocosity, and decided to herself that she preferred a bout of politics of the more overt kind. She felt that she would have to agree with Mrs Bluett, who had once said to her that when Uncle Bert was in a joky mood, you could depend on it that there was 'madness in his melody'. What had he been up to?

The day of the funeral dawned bright but very cold. May was most concerned at the determination of the two old ladies to be outside, at the gate, when the cortège passed. She made all sorts of suggestions about clearing space in the window of Aunt Mabel's downstairs room, but to no avail. Occasions when they could watch the passing of a coffin without peeping from behind closed curtains and pulled blinds were very few. Aunt Mabel had made up her mind. 'We shall draw all the front blinds,' she said. 'An' I'm going to be where I can pull myself up so as I can stand when the coffin goes by. Nobody shall say as me an' my family didn't know how to show their proper respects on a day like this. When my dear ol' mother were being carried to 'er grave, we met the Duke on horseback, comin' home from a meet. He stopped his horse, and pulled it into a gateway. Then he got off, an' stood aside its 'ead, an' as soon as the coffin got near 'im, 'e took 'is 'at off, and 'eld it against his chest, an' bowed 'is 'ead. I shall never forget it. My old mother would ha' been so pleased, if she could ha' knowed. So I shall do the same for 'im, bless his old heart, at least for as long as my poor old legs 'll 'old me up.'

Ruth nodded her agreement. 'So shall I,' she said. 'After all I've bathed him, an' fed 'im, an' changed 'is diaper, an' loved 'im as if he were my own. It's like one o' my own sons going to his last restin' place.'

May compromised on chairs at the gate, with rugs and stone

hot-water bottles. They were both ready inside the house, at least an hour before there was any need, muffled to the eyes in extra clothes. May would close the shop at the appropriate time, and pull down all the blinds.

Mrs Bluett paid them a last-minute visit, before going home to change her apron and put on the hat she only ever wore at weddings and funerals. Her mobile face was pulled into even more grimaces than usual by her attempts to make her expression match the sorrowfully excited mood of the day.

'I only hope as 'e *is* dead,' she trumpeted. 'You can't never be too sure, when folks die as sudden as that. I 'ad an aunt as used to suffer from cattle-heptic fits. Twice they 'ad 'er in 'er coffin. They'd ha' buried 'er, the second time, if it hadn't ha' been for my mother, what was 'er sister-in-law. She went to view her, in 'er box, and she see 'er chest 'eave. She shrieked out: "Don't screw 'er down, she ain't dead!" An' the undertaker's men, they all laughed, an' said they were in an 'urry, 'cos they'd got another one to deal with. But my mother wouldn't give in. She writ something on a bit o' paper, an' said to my uncle, as were my aunt's 'usband, "Tom, you take this subscription round to the chemist, an' bring it back as fast as you can." Well, 'e did, and my mother 'eld the stuff as he got under my aunt's nose, an' she set up in 'er coffin, right as rain.'

This sort of tale was sure to hold its hearers spellbound. 'Yes, poor old Aunt Polly! She didn't live all that long afterwards though. One of 'er neighbours as she were very fond of run her breast against a clo-'e's-prop, and it all multified into a cancer, so as she died. My aunt went to bid her farewell as she laid in her coffin, an' she leaned over an' kissed 'er. An, yer see, she caught the corpse's breath, an' catched a cancer with it, on'y the one she caught were in her bowels! Lorks, I shall have to go, or I shan't get back in time to see the funeral after all.'

'One funeral always puts you in mind o' a lot o' other fun'rals,' Ruth was saying. 'It's only five year since I buried Johnno.'

'He were a pleasant corpse, I know,' said Aunt Mabel. 'I

hope you ain't going to tell me now as you grieved over 'im!'

Ruth shook her head. 'No,' she said, 'he were a real trial, at the last. Would get up an' get dressed, so as 'e could lay on the old sofa where he could keep his eye on me. He'd never eat nothing when I were havin' mine, but as soon as I'd finished an' set down, he'd say, "Wife, I'll 'ev a bit o' fish, now," even though he knowed very well as I couldn't get fish any day only Thursday. Sometimes I used to wish as every mouthful 'e did have would choke him!' She looked round; there was nobody but Aunt Mabel in the shop. May had gone to change, and Uncle Bert was not to be seen. She leaned forward as far as her chair would let her, and Aunt Mabel turned up her earphone in anticipation.

'One day, when 'e were real bad, the doctor 'ad been, an' told me he wouldn't last more than another week or two. Then Johnno laid on that sofa an' called me all the names 'e could think of. Of course everything 'as 'appened to 'im 'ad always been my fault. Then 'e says, all different-like, and sorry for hisself, "Wife, I could do with a hard-b'iled egg to eat." He'd took to havin' eggs 'ard-b'iled, 'cos 'e could eat 'em with 'is fingers, without settin' up. So I got 'im it, and went an' set down in my chair again. I were just nodding off, like, when 'e begun to make such a row, I couldn't think what were the matter. I clawed up an' went to 'im, an' if 'e 'adn't got that there egg stuck half way down 'is gullet! I couldn't lift 'im up, an' I couldn't get 'old o' the egg, 'cos it were so slippy. An' then it come over me, the number o' times as I had wished e'd choke hisself! And 'ere 'e 'ad, well, half-done it, as you might say, with a hard-b'iled egg!'

'Whatever did you do?' said Aunt Mabel, all eyes and ears.

'I got a tea-spoon,' said Ruth, 'an' I give that there egg a good shove, to make sure as 'e couldn't cag it up! Accidental death, the doctor says—but he didn't order no inquest. Said he were as good as dead a'ready anyway.' The blue eyes sparkled with pleasure. She went on. 'An' when it come to it, he hadn't left me a penny. Not a penny! We'd had a bit o' money put by—mostly what I'd earned goin' out washing. But it were in his name, an' after he were dead I found out as 'e'd been spendin' it little by little for years, till it had all gone. If it hadn't ha' been for the insurance I'd got on him, he'd ha' had to be buried by the parish. But I had a hundred pound to come from the insurance, so I was able to bury him real proper. Beautiful oak coffin, I had for 'im. An' when I'd paid everything up, there were just five pound left. So I used that to buy myself a grave in with him!' She sat back, in a glow of deep satisfaction. Aunt Mabel exploded.

'Why, you silly old fool!' she said. 'You can't be in your right mind! To think o' the misery 'e put you through for sixty year or more, an' then you spend the last five pound you had in the world to be put in with 'im!'

Ruth rocked complacently. When Aunt Mabel's indignation had silenced her, Ruth nodded and leaned forward again.

'They buried him atop of his father,' she said. 'You remember him, when he lived with Johnno and me after we were married—the muckiest, foulest-mouthed, cruellest ol' sod as God ever made, 'e were. Then they put my Johnno in with him, an' there were still room for one more. That's 'ow it is in them big new cemeteries nowadays. You can't even 'ev a grave to yourself! An I stood aside the grave as they let Johnno down in 'is box, and I said to myself, "There lay my two worst enemies. They kept topside o' me all the days o' their lives—but I'll be topside o' them at the last that I will!"''

May heard them both chuckling as she came downstairs.

'Come on,' she said. 'Time to get outside. Folks are beginning to gather.'

The boys from the lower school were being placed in position along the route. There happened to be one each side of the shop gate, part of a line that ran right up to the church. Behind the boys the people from the village, all soberly clad, were taking their places. May brought out two kitchen chairs, and placed them inside the wooden palings before bringing out the two old ladies, well muffled with extra shawls. It took a good deal of fuss, before Aunt Mabel was settled to her liking. Once seated, she found her view of the road partially obstructed by the back of the boy on the side of the gate. She poked him in the back with her walkingstick, and having got his attention at last, commanded, 'Move along, can't you? There's other folks than you who want to see!' She continued her harassment until the embarrassed child broke rank, and moved nearer to the one on his left. This immediately brought a stern command from the master in charge, so the boy moved back. Aunt Mabel poked again, at which the master came across the road. The change on Aunt Mabel's visage had to be seen to be believed. Her face broadened into a simpering one-sided smile, as she tilted her head backwards in a series of little jerks, to have it ready to bring down in a gracious, regal sort of nod as she said, 'How-do-you-do?' to the master, with all the air of Queen Mary acknowledging the cheers of a crowd in the Mall. A compromise having been reached between Aunt Mabel and the master, they settled down to wait. May stood in front of the closed door of the shop. Uncle Bert was nowhere to be seen. He'd been out in the morning and had come back with his one and only friend, and both of them had retired to the workshop down the garden. May had completely forgotten them.

The sound of muffled drums reached them first, and the boys came stiffly to attention. Then the black horses came into view, the drums fell into silence, and the only sound to be heard was the creaking of the wheels of the wagon and the clip-clop of heavy hooves on the rough road. They amplified the silence, as it were; it was as if the village had suspended its breathing as in the two-minute silence on Armistice Day. When the horses were fifty yards or so distant, the two old ladies took hold of the railings in front of them, and heaved themselves to their feet. The movement cloaked them with the dignity of old age, and made of them impressive figures. Ruth was wiping away her tears, saying, 'My little Robbie' again and again under her breath. The tears rolled unchecked

107

down Aunt Mabel's face, as she murmured, 'God rest his soul. Amen!' The coffin was now almost in front of them. Ruth dropped into an old-fashioned curtsey, and whispered, 'Goodbye my boy'—and then it happened. The silence was shattered by the sound of a window being thrown open. Every head turned to stare at a point directly above May's head, and behind the backs of the two old women. Out of the dormer window came the heads and shoulders of Uncle Bert and his communist crony. Each waved a flag of brilliant red from side to side as they broke loudly, if untunefully, into the strains of the 'Internationale'.

Over the rest of the day's doings in the shop, let time draw a decent veil.

8 A friend in need . . .

A village is like a kaleidoscope. The removal of a large colour-ful piece changes the detail, but the pattern re-forms without it. There had been time, now, for the Duke's death to be assimilated, and the spectacle and heightened emotion of the funeral had done its cathartic work well. 'Life is uncertain and death sure' is part of the countryman's philosophy. Spirits were gradually rising, and tentative steps into the future were once more being taken.

At The Star, on the evening of the funeral, the gloom seemed to have lifted from everybody except ' 'Appy 'Arry', who sat in his usual corner of the taproom in most unwonted silence, staring over his beer mug into the fire.

'Aye, it'll be a reet old stinger tonight,' said Timmy, com-ing in and holding blue hands to the blaze. 'It's nowt but just past eight, an' it'd freeze the hairs off a gooseberry a'ready.'

'Did you watch the funeral, Timmy? I never clapped eyes on you, from where I stood.' (George Willis.)

'Aye. I couldn't miss champion turn-out like that.'

'Aye! I must say as it put me in mind an' all of owd Bob Murphy's funeral. There must ha' bin nigh on a score o' the Murphy family, altogether. Irish, a good way back, yer know, but they'd lived Sheffle-Rotheram way for two or three generation. All the lot of 'em worked int'pits, an' they could all take a fair drop to drink. When they growed up, some of 'em moved to other pits, like, and then Bob got hurt in a fall, an' after a bit, 'e died. So 'is brothers made up their minds to fetch him home to give 'im proper burial, like. They borrowed t'church hand-bier, and about ten of 'em set out to bring him back. When they got t't village wheer 'e lived, they all went for a drink or two afore setting off back wi' t't coffin.

'It were 'ard work, yer know, an' they took pushin' t'cart in turn. So by the time they reached next village, they were ready for another pint. They tossed up to see which two should stop outside wi' Bob, and the others went int'pub. Come the next pub on't road, they on'y left one brother outside wi't coffin. Then they went on again t'next village, up a reet steep hill, that 'ad a pub at top. When they got theer, oldest says, "Our Bob were allus one to look after hissen. He'll be champion left outside wi'out us." So they left coffin on t'bier, and all went in for another. After several pints, away they went again, an' got t't pub at far end o't same village. This time one o' the young 'uns said, "I reckon our Bob wouldn't think nowt on us leavin' 'im outside while we all 'av a pint. Aye, I'm sure he'd want ter coom inside wi' us." So they took t'coffin in, an' stood it up against wall by't side o't bar. They were nearly back home then—it were on'y t'next village as they'd got to go to. So they stopped an' ad several more an' got to arguin' about racin' pigeons and whippets and the like. At last off they all got up and went towards 'ome, still arguin'.

'It had been arranged as they were to put bier wi' t'coffin on it in t'church till next day. So the parson were on t'look out for 'em, an' come to meet 'em when 'e see 'em coming.

' "Wheer's Bob?" he asks, when he see bier. "By goles," said Micky. "If we ain't left our Bob in't Marquis o' Granby!" '

'Ah, I dessay the old duke would be glad of a nip o' whisky tonight, down in that vault,' said Bill Storey.

There was a growl from 'Appy's corner, as if a sleeping dog had been trodden on.

'You keep a civil tongue in yer 'ead, Bill Storey,' said 'Arry. 'I ain't going to sit 'ere an' 'ear nobody makin' fun o' His Grace. Me an' 'im were boys together. Many's the time we've 'ad to run away from his father's keepers, when I were teachin' 'im how to poach. We 'ad a laugh about it the last time I see 'im, 'bout a month ago. But never no more!'

The company was sobered. They respected 'Arry's personal grief for his boyhood friend.

'He's beyond all your worriting about 'im now, 'Arry,' said George Willis. 'Drink up, an' I'll buy you another.' Practical sympathy was all they knew how to offer. 'Arry drank up. His glass was refilled again and again, till only he was left.

'Finish your drink, 'Arry. It's past closin' time,' said Charlie. 'Arry drank up, and rose unsteadily to his feet. 'Watch your step,' Charlie added. 'It'll be slippery outside by now.'

'Arry put on his old cap, and went out into the moonlight. Charlie kept an eye on him till he reached the crossroads. From there he had only a couple of hundred yards to go to his tiny cottage up 'the little lane' that led to the back of Cudweed Farm.

The little lane was not a made-up road. There were huge pot-holes all over it, and a deep grip under the hedge on each side. Almost at his own gate, 'Arry stumbled and fell, rolling off the path and into the ditch.

It was Bill Storey who found him next morning, on his way to work at 5.00 am. His lantern picked out a dark patch among the rime, and he swung it up to see clearer. 'Appy lay with his backside in the ditch, his head under the hedge and his feet on the path at the other side of the grip. There was hoar frost on his cap, and on the ends of the neckerchief tied round his scraggy neck. The water over his body had formed solid ice all round him, and his white-rimed limbs were frozen to the ground; but he was still breathing. Bill turned and ran as fast as he could back to the schoolhouse, where one of the few telephones the village boasted was installed, and knocked Miss Taylor into wakefulness. She sent for doctor and nurse, in case one or the other could not come at once. Then, rousing Miss Nellie, the three of them set off with blankets and thermos flasks of hot water to set the prisoner free. By the end of the day, he was installed in the local union workhouse, reviling everyone who had not left him to thaw out in peace and go home when he was ready.

'Interfering buggers,' he said over and over again. 'They wouldn't ha' dared to do it, if His Grace were still alive. 'E wouldn't ha' let them bring me 'ere!'

He was probably right; but the old order had passed, and given way to new. He just happened to be its first victim.

Nurse Hardy had been their district nurse for nearly twenty years, the first of such beings they had ever encountered. She had arrived, a stranger from London, and about twenty-five—plump, dark and rosy, neat, trim and handsome in her navy-blue uniform with its pert little round hat which bore the badge of her training hospital on the front.

Three villages were put under her care, and she was given a council house in the middle one, with a cycle at her disposal on which to reach the other two. The people in her district viewed her advent with satisfaction, and her person with a mixture of resentment and awed respect. She was the embodiment of hygiene, and cleanliness seemed to crackle from her starched white apron, collar and cuffs when she took off her coat in a cramped old cottage bedroom. It was soon evident that in spite of her smiling, even mischievous face and eyes, there was a stern disciplinarian standing in her flat black shoes. When she reached the side of a woman in labour, it was like a captain coming aboard his flagship. Fidgeting husbands were sent about their business with a few terse orders; fussing or tearful mothers were sent on totally unnecessary errands to keep them out of the way; nosey friends or officious village midwives were dispatched with little ceremony. For the patients alone was the voice softened, the touch gentled, and strength and comfort poured out from full bosom and sturdy arms. To them she seemed like a harbour light; offering help, direction, and above all, security. After the event, they were not quite so sure of their opinion about her. 'Thinks herself everybody, with her London ways,' was more than one ungrateful woman's verdict, once she held her baby in her arms.

The men soon found much to admire in her, partly because she was a woman of a kind they did not often meet, but mostly because of her dauntless courage, physical as well as moral. The blackest night, the foulest weather, the greatest distance, the filthiest bedroom never deflected her from duty. If the conditions were such that she could not cycle, she walked—across ploughed fields in midwinter, through lonely lanes and woodland paths in the dead of a summer's night, clutching a lantern in one hand and her little black bag in the other.

She was known, universally, simply as 'Nurse'. Once she was established, she was taken more or less for granted, and her efficient good nature much abused. Doctors were scarce, and had to be paid, even when they could do no good. 'Nurse' was free, and was often sent for in lieu of paying the doctor. She protested a good deal about this, explaining patiently that her function was midwifery and the nursing of the sick when the doctor requested such attention for his patients. But the villages made up their minds that all children and all old folks were within her province, whatever was the matter with them; then women who 'didn't like to talk to the doctor' about their ailments consulted her instead (and saved a fee), while men tended to insist on calling her out 'because they didn't like to worry' the doctor. As a result, she was very overworked, and often in hot water with the medical men, though they had to admit that the situation was none of her making. She had gathered that it was usually a case of sending for her, or no one; and the number of times she had been in the nick of time to send for the doctor herself, and thereby avert tragedy, was growing steadily. Unless she was physically unable to be in two places at once, she answered every call. If she didn't, the women in particular were soon up in arms, and discussed her failings resentfully round Charlie's pump or in the shop.

Twenty years is usually enough for any stranger to become integrated into the heart of the community; but 'Nurse' had the disadvantage of living in one community, while serving three. The one in which she lived wanted her all to themselves; the other two felt it wasn't fair that she should belong to the church, the WI and so on, in the village she lived in. Still, wherever she went in any of her rôles, she was usually welcome. In her early days among them, she had been found willing to help entertain at socials, and was a mine of ideas for getting the young folk of the village to make their own pleasures—hence the concert party 'The Magpies', which was fast gaining a reputation over a wide area.

She had put on a lot of weight in twenty years, but in other respects was much the same woman as she had been when she had first arrived. The cycle had been supplemented by a small car, but she still rode her old upright bike, declaring that it would take her to places across field paths and so on where no car could go.

She had won her spurs in the village after only one year's probation, when poor little Glenys Foreman met with her misfortune. Glenys was only a baby in arms when the accident happened. Her sister had got her out for a walk in the pram, when one of the horses from Glebe Farm had bolted with its heavy cart full of sacks of potatoes. The man in charge of it had got down to open the gate from the field to the road, and nobody ever knew what caused the horse to run away. In vain the chap had shouted 'Whoa! Whoa!' when it began to move, and in vain he had begun to run, to try and catch the bridle, or jump up on the cart to get the reins. Once on the road, the horse had begun to gallop, throwing the cart and its load from side to side of the road. The dreadful noise of hooves clanking and iron rims rattling on the granite of the road, had warned the older child of something amiss, and she had pulled the baby from the pram to get as far off the road as she could. But when the horse was just passing the children, it caught its foot in the loose rein and fell, tipping the cart over. The older girl had escaped injury, other than bruising, but the baby had been knocked from her arms, and the wheel of the cart had pinned the tiny leg to the ground.

Nurse had arrived before the doctor, but both could see that a miracle would be needed if ever the baby were ever now to walk. The local hospital had done its best, but Glenys had come home with ankle and foot so misshapen as to douse all hopes. It was then that Nurse had shown both her enormous compassion and her practical, unwearying tenacity. Barely a day passed when she did not find time to call at the cottage, and do what she could for the welfare of the baby. The parents, in their grief and distress, looked to her visits for their moral sustenance, her cheerful warmth leaving behind far more comfort than the parson's stumbling words of Christian philosophy. There seemed some danger that the limb was not growing to match the other. Nurse took it upon herself to massage it daily, whenever the press of other work allowed. When Glenys began to hobble about, Nurse's visits were the high spot of her existence. It was Nurse who persuaded Miss Taylor to take the child into school before she reached statutory age, thereby creating a bond of sympathy between them, as well as ensuring for Glenys another protector.

When she was seven, the local hospital declared there was nothing more they could do, so Nurse and Miss Taylor between them hatched a scheme, and one day set off with Glenys to see the most famous orthopaedic surgeon in London. Glenys was eventually admitted to a London hospital for surgery, and was home again a year later, walking properly, but with a heavy blocked boot and caliper. She would now at least be able to live an almost normal life.

She was a pretty, delicately moulded child with a yellow

head, like a cowslip—frail but full of life, and because of her disability she became a sort of charge on the corporate sympathy of the village. In the same way, the corporate gratitude was extended to Nurse. Glenys had taken her place in school, making light of her boot and caliper except for odd moments, as when Miss Taylor asked for a 'composition' on 'My Greatest Wish.' The teacher was always saddened to read such open self-expression as 'My greatest wish is to have a pair of white satin slippers to wear at parties'. Glenys was now grown up, and at work in the town, though her family still lived in the village, to which Glenys came for occasional weekends and holidays. Nurse had still had one card up her sleeve. The surgeon had said that when growth was completed, there might possibly be hope of a final operation for a bit more improvement on the mangled ankle bones. Nurse had kept this information to herself, at least till Glenys was eighteen. When it was then put to the girl, she had declined to go through with any more treatment. Since then, there had been a slight change in their relationship. Glenys was declaring independence, and Nurse judged this to be good, though sad at its results. She had taken her finger out of the pie. But the village had noticed nothing, especially as Nurse by that time was earning further gratitude and admiration by her constant care for Jack Marriatt's dying wife.

When she had first come among them, there had been many who had wondered aloud why she had not married. As she was not forthcoming about her private life they were forced to discover, or invent it, for themselves. Discovery was a bit more difficult than usual, since all they had to go on was that she was a Cockney born, she said, 'within the sound of Bow bells'. Their acquaintance with that part of the world being nil, they were forced back on invention. Where the tale started, no one knew; but it was soon established as a 'fact' that she had been engaged to a doctor in the army, who had been killed and posthumously awarded the VC for bravery. The details of his exploit grew with every telling, and much maudlin sympathy was expended on the non-existent doctor, as well as on his faithful bereaved fiancée.

'She don't wear no rings, though,' Aunt Mabel had once said to Mrs Watson.

'Dearie me O, of course she don't. Nurses ain't allowed to wear no jewell'ry!' That settled that. Somewhat more difficult to account for was her flippant reply to Margie's mother, who, watching her bath, kiss and cuddle a newborn baby, remarked to her what a pity it was that she 'hadn't none of her own'. She had looked up and said, 'Good heavens, Mrs Scott! Don't wish me that! You can't have babies without a man as well. In my work I see too much of women who've got men to want one of them for my own!'

It was duly reported, with additions. 'An' she says, "Good God, Missus, I don't want no man near me! I wouldn't take one if he were stuffed wi' gold. Men only want one thing," she says, "an' from what I see o' things, some of 'em only 'ave to 'ang their trousers over the end o' the bed and they have to send for me again! I never could abide men," she says, "an' I never shall be able to".'

It was certainly a puzzle but, as Sally Woods said, perhaps she talked like this to cover up her broken heart.

It was, therefore, a great fillip to the perpetual interest in Nurse's private life when Elsie Winters hinted darkly that she had heard a thing or two, that she could tell them, if she would. Aunt Mabel could hardly bear the frustration of not knowing all there was to know, and cornered Elsie one day so neatly that she gleaned enough to go on, and the seed of a really good new crop of romantic additions to the defunct fiancé theory.

'Well, you see,' said Elsie in a stage whisper, 'now and again when Jack Marriatt's wife were laying bad abed, she'd meet the doctor up at Cudweed. One day when I see 'is car outside the door, I made it my business to go up there to ask him for some more med'cine for Perce's bad back—just in case 'e should get it again like 'e did last year, you understand. So I were waiting outside the door when the doctor and Nurse come out together. He were still talking, an' with my own ears I 'eard 'im say, "There's nothing more we can do, Mrs Hardy," 'e says. "It won't be long now before the end." It's as true as I stand 'ere, he called her Missus Hardy! I were so took back, I couldn't for the life of me remember what it was as I'd gone up to ask 'im for, and 'e were real short with me for wasting his valuable time. But you could ha' knocked me down with a feather. I've never told nobody before, because it isn't any of my business, and as you know I don't talk scandal. But you may depend upon it that all her particulars had to go in front o' the doctors afore she could be given her job, so of course he'd know as she had been married. Fancy her being able to keep it to herself like that all these years!'

So she was not a broken-hearted fiancée, but a bereaved war widow? Poor thing! Aunt Mabel was in her glory, at having this mite of gossip to disseminate. Two days later, Mrs Bluett reported to her neighbour:

'Only married twenty-four hours they were, before he had to go back to France. And then he were killed by one o' them trench-mortals. And they say that when she got the telegram, she went off in a swound, an' never come round for three days. An' when at last she did, she told everybody never to mention her husband again. She'd keep her memories of 'im to 'erself, she said, and never let nobody know as she'd ever been married. She said she'd be a 'moffradite, as couldn't abear men, in future, an' live an' die an old maid'.

Utterly oblivious of her awful fate Nurse had simply continued to go about her business. She was on her way to visit Miss Nellie about the Mothers' Union social, when she happened to meet Reggie Pettigrew. He was standing outside Don's shop by The Star, deep in conversation with Sammy Gaskin.

'Hold on a minute, Sam,' Reg said. 'I want to hear the end of the tale, but I must have a word with Nurse.' He called out to her, and she good-naturedly got off her old bike and joined them. Sam was not to be put off from finishing his anecdote. Reg just had time to greet Nurse properly, and tell her he had need of her help and advice, before Sammy, delighted with an extra listener, launched forth again.

'I s'll have to go back a bit, so's Nurse knows what I'm talkin' about,' he said.

'Yer see, when I were a young chap, there were a lot of us as used to work together, takin' jobs by piece-work wheer ever we could get it. It warn't no way for a married man to go on, but them as were still single used to enj'y it. We went from farm to farm don't yer see, an' we allus used to try to get the hay work done round here, in time to go up to the haylands round London—places like Finchley and Barnet, and such like. Well, one year all our mates had got married, only me and another chap called Joby Parker, so there were only two of us to go London way. We set out to walk to London, sleepin' rough on the way, like we all'us did. It used to take us three or four days to get as far as the haylands, don't yer see—but it were a real outin' for us, and we looked forrard to it all the year. On'y this year as I'm tellin' you about, we were in a bit o' trouble, 'cos we didn't know the way without our mates. We got on all right for the first day an' night, but the next day we got goin' through some heathland and walked for miles and miles without comin' to a village or meetin' anybody we could ask the way from. When it begun to get dark, I 'appened to think as we might be going away from London, instead o' towards it, and I said to Joby as we should have to find out some'ow wheer we were, and which way to go. Then Joby looks all round, and says, "Let's keep going, my 'earty. I reckon there's a waypost atop o' that next 'ill." So up we went, an' there the waypost stood. Then Joby says, "What's the bugger say, Sammy?" An' that put me in a fix, 'cos I weren't much of a reader. Well—to tell you the truth, I ain't never learned no more than S for Sammy an' G for Gaskin, all my life. But I were surprised as Joby warn't no better scholar. "Can't yer read it, then, Sam?" says Joby anxious-like. I went an' looked at it real close, an' I said, "There's a Hess, I know that, an' I kin see a Gee on this 'ere other arm, but I can't make nothing else out about what them other figures mean." So there we stood, an' didn't know which o' the four roads to take no more than if there hadn't ha' bin a waypost there at all. Then at last Joby says, "I know what, Sam. We're got our tools with us, ain't we? Let's dig the bloody thing up and take it with us, till we do meet somebody as can read it for us!" '

Reggie was grinning delightedly. He would have stood there all day, provided Sam's fund of anecdotes didn't run out, if his time had not been quite so valuable. Today, he had other things on his mind.

'I'll see you again another day, Sam,' he said. 'I want to have a bit of a word with Nurse, now she's here.'

Sammy accepted the dismissal, and Reg and Nurse moved off together, Nurse pushing her bike.

'It's about them diddikies over in the cottage the far side o' the woods,' he said. 'They camped in there in 'tater-picking time, and never went off when the others did. There's a whole hussle of 'em, but I don't know if they're all one family or not. The chap didn't seem to be a bad worker when he were in the gang 'tater-picking, so I thought I might give him a regular job till they could find somewhere else to go. But he wouldn't have it—he says regular work don't agree with him, and that he's got a certificate to say his lungs are bad, so as he mustn't work when it's wet or cold or when it's hot, or there's dust blowing. That don't leave him a lot o' chance to kill himself with work. So there they are, on my land, in a cottage that ain't fit for a pigsty, and I don't know how to get rid of 'em. Marston never lets me alone about it, now he's in charge o' the estate. I shall have to put 'em out on the road, I reckon, to please him, before I'm done. But that's why I wanted to see you.

'I went up there yesterday, to catch the chap an' talk to him—his name's Sid Roslin. As a rule, as soon as I get anywhere near the place, the kids all fly inside an' bang the door, so as you don't see nobody but Sid. I tried to make it plain to him yesterday that they couldn't stop there. He's as slippery as an eel—all he'd keep saying was, "Yes, sir, I know as it ain't fit to live in. That's what I say. We shall 'ev to get out. You'll 'ev to find us alternative accommodation," he says.

' "Don't you come that," I says. "You ain't one o' my workmen. If you'd took the job I offered you, it would be different."

' "It's your cottage we're a livin' in," Sid says. "We can't go till we've got somewheer to go to, can we? You'll have to go to the council, and get them to give us a house."

' "I tell you, Sid," I said. "It's none o' my business where you go, but you can't stop here."

' "No, Sir," he says. "I know we can't. It ain't fit for no decent family to live in. That's what I say. Disgustin', I call it, for farmers to let their property get into such a state, an' then expect decent folks to live in it. So as soon as you can get us another house," he says, "we'll move." An' there he stood, smoking fags one after the other—and had the cheek to ask me to look at the old car he's bought "to see what's wrong with it 'cos it don't go very well".

'It's a capper, I reckon, when a chap like him can have a car, an' run it! But such as him always have ways and means o' getting things without paying for 'em. That's what makes Marston so mad. Sid Roslin needs a car to take the pheasants what he's poached where 'e can sell 'em.

'I know as I made a bad mistake in not turnin' 'em out before the winter come—or having 'em in the first place. But it was because of Marston being so awkward in the first place that made me think of offering him a job! I couldn't get sense out of Sid at all, though, and everything I told him about getting off my land were like water on a duck's back. Anyway—that's my problem. What I wanted to see you about, were different. I've only ever caught sight o' Sid's wife once, an' that were through the window. But while I was talking to Sid yesterday, she opened the door and come out. If you'll excuse the vulgarity, Nurse, I'll say she looks just about ready to kittle again. I don't think I ever did see a woman such a size! I can't put her out on the road in that condition, especially with all the rest o' them little kids. But that place ain't fit for a sow to pig in, let alone a woman. What do you think I ought to do?'

Nurse gave the matter her usual consideration.

'I haven't had any requests for help,' she said. 'And I doubt if they'll send for me. Such folks seem to manage, like animals, by themselves, unless something goes very wrong. Are there any girls big enough to be any good?'

Reg looked worried. 'There's one, about fourteen,' he said. 'But most o' the others seem to be boys. I reckon there must be eight or nine of 'em. Looks as if there's twins about three year old, and another as can only just about walk.'

'Look, don't worry too much, Mr Pettigrew. If anything does go wrong, I don't doubt that I shall soon hear. I'd go round and call, if it wasn't so far and so difficult to get at, but I should very likely only get sworn at for my trouble. But I agree that you can't very well set a woman in that state out on the road. Does Mr Marston know the wife's expecting again? Surely he wouldn't badger you about it if he did? Anyway, let me know if I am needed.'

She got on her bike as Reg lifted his cap, and pedalled off thinking what a nice man he was. Nurse had a fair amount of experience under her starched apron of men like Sid Roslin. She was ready for a cup of tea with Miss Nellie when she finally reached the Schoolhouse.

'I was out all last night,' she said. 'Old Mr Gates died just before midnight, and I'd no sooner got home and into bed than I had to get up again to deliver Vera Blake's baby.'

'Make one, knit two together,' Nellie commented, clicking her knitting needles. Nurse spluttered on her tea. She liked Nellie.

When Reggie got home, he saw Marston's car standing at Stavesacre's front door, and found the agent in the farmyard, making notes in a little book.

'Ah, there you are, Reg,' he said, without looking up. 'I shan't keep you above a few minutes.'

Reg felt his temper rising. Marston was a short, square man, very pink of face and inclined to be pudgy, especially his overclean hands. He was going slightly bald on top, but the rest of his hair was a reasonably thick crop of dark auburn curls. His dress was exaggeratedly rural-genteel, with highly polished brown boots and leggings, expensive breeches and a check tweed jacket. The sight of the agent was enough to raise Reg's hackles, these days. But Reg was further irritated by being addressed by his Christian name. Of course he was 'Reg' to nearly everybody in the village, even some of his workmen. He liked it that way, though it infuriated Gwen to hear them address him so. He could not put on airs, if his life depended on it, and never pretended to be other than he was, a struggling tenant farmer now at last beginning to be able to show you two ten-shilling notes for a pound. The Duke had called him 'Pettigrew'—but then, he called the agent 'Marston'. Reg was acutely aware that Marston had addressed him to his face as 'Reg'. It rankled. He counter-attacked immediately.

'What's the matter this time, then—Derek?' he asked. Marston's face was a study, reddening and clouding in a way that boded Reg no good.

'I'm just making notes of all dilapidations to date,' he said. 'By the terms of your contract, you are responsible for all dilapidations, you know.'

'Only if and when I leave,' said Reg.

'Yes, of course. But we don't know what's going to happen now, do we? Circumstances alter cases. The new duke may sell, or insist on you having a new contract; or even decide to farm Stavesacre himself again, like they did until you came. You'll have to get that barn done up, before valuation. And that set of stables. Wants two or three hundred pound spending on it, at least. I'd better see Ted Lillywhite about getting it done.'

'You better hadn't!' said Reg. 'They were in that condition

when I took 'em over, and I ain't paying no fancy prices to have 'em done up. I'm sick o' your bloody interfering already.'

'Don't you swear at me, my good man! I won't have it!'

'No, and I won't have you telling me what to do, contract or no contract. So get off my land, quick as you can! D'you hear?' Reg was fighting for self-control. He knew it would make a delicate situation worse for him to bandy words with the agent, but the cork was nearly out of his bottled Irish temper.

'I shall go when I've finished what I came to do,' retorted Marston, ostentatiously shifting his position to get a good view of the roof of the cowsheds. Just then, the back door of the house opened, and Gwen appeared. She was dressed in a pretty afternoon frock, hair and make-up all in place. She didn't see her husband, but called out in a lah-di-dah voice to Marston.

'The tea is made, Mr Marston. Do come in and have a cup.'

'Thank you. I'll be there in a moment.'

Reg swung round, his eyes blazing and fire in his face. 'If you ain't out o' my house, and off my land in ten minutes,' he said. 'I'll break your bloody neck. An' I shall wait here with my watch in my 'and, to time you.'

He pulled out from his waistcoat pocket a silver watch, and held it face up in his left hand. His face now wore a look of unholy glee, his grey eyes glinting like granite. He grasped his knobbly ash stick firmly in his right hand, and set his feet apart for a well-balanced stance.

'Ten minutes from now,' he said. 'Take your time to make up your mind. You can't say as I'm hurrying you. That's one minute gone,' he added, as Marston hesitated, wondering what sort of a match he'd be for the tough farmer. He thought he might stand a good chance of coming off top dog, for he had had a grammar school education, which had included the rudiments of boxing. He guessed Reg had plenty of strength, but no science. On the other hand, he felt his dignity was above brawling with a tenant farmer. But how could he retreat now, without losing face everywhere when the tale was told?

'Two minutes gone,' said Reg, implacably.

Marston made for the door of the house. If he accepted the invitation of Reg's wife, Reg could hardly attack him in her view, in his own sitting-room.

The same thought had occurred to Reg. He didn't know how to get out of the situation either, and commonsense was fast returning to him.

From the front of the house came the furious honking of a car's horn.

'That's my car,' said Marston, making off towards it. 'Somebody wants me, no doubt.' Reggie followed. He wanted to make sure the agent was gone in the remaining six minutes or so. When they reached the front of the house though, both men began to run. The drive from house to road sloped gently down hill for fifty yards or so, bordered by shrubs. Marston had left his car facing the porch of the house. Behind the wheel of it was Angie, punching the bulb of the horn and uttering shrieks of fiendish delight every time she succeeded in making it work. When Marston came into view, she used both hands to release the hand brake, and the car started to move backwards down the slope. As it gathered speed, she hung on to the wheel again, and it careered from side to side in a crazy zigzag.

Luckily, she directed it into a clump of bushes before it reached the wide gate. Reg ran in fear to reach his angel child. Marston ran swearing, to rescue his car. By the time they reached her, Angie had taken a severe bump in the face from the wheel, and had put a sharp little tooth into her bottom lip. All anger forgotten at the sight of blood down her dress, Reg lifted her clear. Marston stood back holding the car door, deafened by Angie's screams. The two men glared at each other for a split second—long enough for Angie to sum up the situation. She stopped in mid-scream, and over Reg's shoulder as he turned spat accurately into Marston's face. He climbed into the car, and prayed urgently that the self-starter would work. It did. The gears ground as he manoeuvred the car out of the bushes, shaking his fist at Reg's back. But Reg had reached the house laughing, all anger forgotten in his triumphant memory of the blood spattered down Marston's expensive tie.

'That'll teach him, won't it, my pretty,' he said. By the time he'd cleaned Angie up, he was himself again. Gwen always conveniently felt sick at the sight of blood, and in caring for Angie Reg forgot her too. Nevertheless, he felt a sense of uneasy stalemate. The game was by no means finished.

9 A little help's worth a lot of pity

The kitchen at Stavesacre was cheerfully chaotic on Saturday evening, when Jacky Roslin knocked. Roddy, on his way out, let the child in. The boy was embarrassed, confused, and awed. He was wet through, and held his ragged coat together with one dirty paw; he kept half-raising the other into the air, like a child in school awaiting permission to 'leave the room'.

'What's the matter, sonny? What do you want?'

'Please, sir, dad says can somebody go and fetch the nurse, 'cos our mam's took bad.'

Reg understood the situation at once, and cursed his luck that Roddy and the motorbike had escaped too soon to be of use. He knew that Gwen would resent any slight delay, or his involvement in any way with matters other than her enjoyment. He thought quickly.

'Now listen hard,' he said. 'We are just going out for the evening, and it will be bull's noon before we get back. I can't fetch Nurse for you, though I will call at her house and tell her she's needed. But it is a terrible night, and I reckon she'll have to walk up to your place through the wood and across the field. Tell your dad he must go and meet her at the gate that goes into the wood—he'll know his way well enough. Roly, get the stable lantern and light it. What's your name? Jack?

Well, you take my lantern and get off back home as soon as you can. If you go now, and your dad starts out straight away, Nurse'll be there as soon as he is—well, that is if she isn't out somewhere else already.'

The lighted lantern was passed to the boy, who waited for no more.

Reg and Gwen put on their coats and Reg manoeuvred the car up to the porch so that Gwen got in without getting wet.

'I really shall have to get the phone laid on,' he said, following his own thoughts. 'I don't like being out of reach all the rest of the night.'

'If you're concerned more about that diddiki family than me,' Gwen replied, 'you can come back when you're ready to. You needn't bother to wait for me, I'm sure Mr Marston would see me home.'

Reg controlled his feelings, telling himself that whatever happened he mustn't let anybody see that Marston's relationship with Gwen riled him. He delivered his message to Nurse, in spite of Gwen's protests that they would be late. 'There's two ways up to the cottage,' he said. 'One of them is a cart track up from the village. That's the longest way round, but in the ordinary way you could get your car right up to the door. I've been thinking about it, though, and after rain like this you'd quite likely get stuck. Then you'd have a lot farther to walk than if you took your car as far as Stavesacre Wood on the other road, and went across the field. I've told Roslin to go down and meet you at the wood with a lantern—and I've lent him the lantern. You may need it up there. I'm afraid you'll find a proper mess up in that cottage.

'I'm sorry I can't do more to help. We shall be out till two o'clock at the earliest, and there's only Margaret left up at Stavesacre. She's looking after Angie, and she'll most likely go to bed when Roly does. It would have to happen tonight.' He could not rid himself of the guilty feeling that he was in some way responsible for Sid Roslin's wife and family's plight. He said as much, to Gwen, when he returned to the car.

128

'I don't know why you bother your head about such low trash,' she said. 'Their goings on are nothing to do with us—well, at least, with me. But you haven't got any pride, and don't care a bit how you let me down, or the children. It's a pity you and Geoff ever left the fens. No wonder you're so ignorant and countrified, when I think about how you were brought up.'

Reg said nothing. He was used to this sort of thing by now, and didn't exert himself to make the obvious replies. It just wasn't worth it.

Nurse collected her things and put them into her car. She looked, as always, as if she had just come from the laundry, clean, starched, crisp and sterile. Experience had taught her that she would probably be away most of the night, so she made what preparations she could for her own comfort when she should return. Then she hurried away, remembering what Reg Pettigrew had said about there being hordes of children already. Sometimes things happened with incredible speed in such cases—as she had said, almost like animals. On the other hand, she had hardly expected to be sent for at all, and certainly she had not been 'booked' by anybody. That could mean unexpected complications.

The wavering light of a lantern being swung from side to side gave her notice that an escort of some sort was waiting at the gate into the woods.

The rain was still teeming down, driven by an icy wind. Roslin was draped all over with sacks, as protection against the wet. He seemed impatient and resentful rather than worried, as Nurse parked her car on the grass verge and prepared herself to face the elements.

'You've been long enough gettin' here,' was his welcome, as she stepped out of the car. 'I thought you were never comin'.'

'I'm only human,' she said, determined not to form opinions too soon, in case they might have to be changed. 'I can't fly, you know. And please remember that I haven't been booked to attend your wife. You're lucky I've come at all. Why have you bothered to send for me now?'

'She's been bad since early mornin', but nothing seems to be 'appening. She's never had no trouble before, not even with the twins. We've never had no call to get a nurse before— there's always been another woman about to see 'er through, other times. I allowed that me and our Sissy could manage this time. Sissy's fourteen turned.'

'We'd better be getting to her, quick as we can,' said Nurse. 'You lead the way with your lantern. I'll follow with mine but you'd better carry my bag. It'll be all I can do to stay on my feet, I think.'

They struck off into the words, and Nurse soon found her prediction accurate. Among the bare trees the rain had less driving force, but the sodden branches dropped huge dollops of water onto them, as if to make up any deficiency of discomfort. These sudden douches were almost worse to endure than steady rain, because they were irregular and unexpected, suddenly slapping into the face, or down inside the collar, or onto unprotected legs and feet. The two lanterns cast only a feeble glow in the pitch-black miasma of darkness, as if defeated by the magnitude of their task before they started. The curved glass protecting the wicks clouded up with patches of irridescent blue haze, and the subdued yellow circles of light bounced like soap bubbles up and down, back and forth, and from side to side. They picked out for a split second an ancient oak root here, the dignity of a grey-green beech trunk there, or the tangled mass of a hawthorn bush straggling across the path. The patch on which no light fell was the yard or so directly in front of the feet, making every step a calculated hazard. A day of rain had turned the narrow path into a greasy cakewalk of a track, sticky with sodden clay and slippery as glass with rotting leaves. Roslin strode on fairly confidently, as one who knew the path he was treading as well in the dark as in daylight. In fact, he found the unaccustomed light of his lantern more confusing than useful. He was well used to negotiating woodland ways in the dark, though even his poaching activities did not usually take him out on so foul a night. Nurse was no tenderfoot in such a situation either, and did her best to keep up with her guide, slipping and using her arms to balance herself, encumbered though she was by her lantern. She had an electric torch in her coat pocket, but she preferred to keep that for real emergency. She did not know yet what the night might bring forth and it was still only about nine o'clock.

The wood petered out at last, and they crossed an enclosing ditch through a gap in a hedge. That brought them out into an open ploughed field. Wind and rain met them again with full force, the pale lanterns now illuminating space crossed with the silver stair-rods of rain. It stung against their faces, and forced their heads down to meet it.

'Bloody woman! It's just like her to choose a night like this to fall to bits,' Roslin said, more to himself than to his companion. Nurse saved her breath for when it should be more needed, and they battled on round the headland of the field, climbing a steady if gentle slope. Once at the top of it, Roslin paused, and pointed. The tiny spark of a candle in a window showed through the murk about two hundred yards distant. Ten minutes later, Nurse was stamping her feet on the cobbled doorway of the cottage. Roslin threw open the door and she stepped inside.

The derelict dwelling was the remains of two cottages, long since abandoned as being too far away from the village. The door led straight into the main room of one of them, from which a few bits and pieces of furniture had never been removed after the death of the last occupant. On the open hearth, the remains of a fire still smouldered. A rickety deal table occupied the middle of the bare brick floor, and standing beside it were three or four orange-boxes that obviously served as stools and benches. One broken wicker armchair stood beside the hearth, and another chair, concocted from an old car-seat placed on a wooden crate, faced it on the other side. Under the window, in which several missing panes had been replaced with wood or cardboard, was a stone sink with a pail of dirty water underneath it. Against the sink stood a tall, thin girl, drying her hands on what appeared to be the remains of a flannel shirt-tail. She had been crying, and her face was smudged with dirt and tears. This must be Sissy. Nurse spoke cheerily to her as she entered, but the girl did not reply, though she turned to face her father with a kind of instinctive movement of defence. She wore a resigned but curiously placid look, in spite of the tears, and it took Nurse no more than one glance to sum the girl up as retarded, perhaps even simple.

'She is bad,' the girl said. 'I'm glad you're come back. I daresn't go in with her no more.'

'Where are the others?' her father asked.

'I put the baby and the twins to bed,' said Sissy. 'The two littl'uns are in there with 'em. There's Jack.' She pointed to a corner by the hearth, where even the combined light of two lanterns and a candle barely reached. Sitting with their backs to the wall were Jacky, nearly naked because he had had to peel off his rainsoaked rags, and the brother next in age to him. They were covered up by sacks and old coats, and Nurse gathered that this was where they slept anyway.

'Where's my patient?' she asked briskly, putting first things first. She removed her dripping uniform coat, and mopped her wet face with a large handkerchief. She discarded her sodden hat, and black curls tinged on the temples with grey now framed her plump face. She pushed them up with her hands, drying the ends of them on the handkerchief. Her starched apron had been pinned up round her waist, to escape the rain. She let it down over her bedraggled skirt, and wished ruefully for some dry slippers. From her bag she took a large linen square and fixed it nurse-fashion over her head. She was ready for action.

Roslin had been divesting himself of wet sacks, and moved to the wicker chair, rousting from it a lean whippet before throwing himself down.

He nodded sideways to one of two doors that stood side by side in the wall opposite to the hearth.

'She's in there,' he said, making no move from the chair. Nurse took bag and lantern, and opened the door she thought had been indicated.

A candle standing in a broken saucer was light enough for her to see her mistake, and to take in the room at a glance. It was absolutely bare except for a cot improvised from a broken drawer, in which lay a toddler, fast asleep. A mattress on the floor by the wall held a twin asleep at each end, and under the dark window, on a pile of sacking, sat two other little boys stolidly munching hunks of bread and dripping.

'Other one,' said Roslin from his chair. Nurse shut the door again, and opened the second.

This room contained the frame of an old iron bedstead, on which a filthy blue and white striped mattress still lay. On the mattress a grey-faced woman rolled from side to side, moaning. She was clad only in a loose day dress, and had kicked off the collection of old shawls, cut-open sacks and thin brown army-type blankets that comprised the bedclothes. Her head lay on a pillow, the dirty dark-grey and black striped ticking throwing into contrast a wealth of beautiful hair so palely golden that it shone like dry straw in autumn sunshine. The plaits had come undone, and the long hair was tangled with sweat across the pain-wracked face. As the spasm passed, the hands clutching her belly unclasped themselves, and Nurse took one of them in her own. The blue eyes of the patient, dark with exhaustion, fluttered open for a moment, but closed again, and she began to snore as nature snatched for her momentary respite between contractions. Nurse laid the hand down, noting as she did so its fine shape and the long filbert nails. Her own experienced hands carried out a swift, revealing, first examination before the legs began to twitch again and the writhing re-commenced. Nurse sat herself down on the filthy mattress, placing her sturdy back against the woman's, and held both hands till the spasm passed again. The dark eyes opened for a moment in grateful wonder, and then closed. Nurse left the bed and went to the connecting door. She looked across at Roslin, dozing in his chair, and anger welled up in her. Striding across to him, she shook him furiously, at which the whippet rose snarling from his side, with bared teeth.

'Come on now, this is no time for taking naps! I need help—urgently. I want a doctor, if there's one to be got. Rouse up and get that car of yours going. Get to the nearest telephone—at the schoolhouse I should think— or go and fetch Dr Leathers yourself. Tell him he must come, quick.'

Roslin roused himself languidly. 'I ain't goin' out no more on a night like this,' he said. 'She'll do all right now you're 'ere. What are you paid for, if we have to have a doctor an' all?'

'I must have a doctor,' she repeated. 'You'll have to try to get out the long way round, but with a car that'll be quicker in the long run than walking all the way. You'll have to risk getting stuck.'

'It ain't no use you standing there bawlin' at me,' he said. 'The bloody car won't go, even if I could get it out to the road after the rain we've 'ad. There's something wrong with it. I reckon the distributor end's wore out.'

'Distributor end! It's your distributor end that ought to be worn out, from what I can see of things! You'll have to walk down to the village, that's all.'

He shook his head. 'I tell yer, I ain't goin' out no more tonight. She'll be all right. She's 'ad plenty o' kids before wi' no trouble.'

He closed his eyes, sticking out his feet almost into the heap of dead ashes on the hearth. The dog crept back to him, and he fondled its ears.

'And I'm telling you, that if you don't get a doctor here soon, your wife will probably die.' From the bedroom the sound of moaning reached her. She darted back to give all the comfort and help that she could, reappearing after two or three minutes. The man was asleep again. Sissy was crying, round-eyed with fear, into the bowl of cold, greasy washing-up water that still stood in the sink. Nurse stepped briskly to the sink, dipped the filthy shirt-tail into the water, and whipping round, brought the full force of it slapping into Roslin's face, once from the left and again from the right. He sprang up with a string of oaths, and snatched it from her, slinging it across the room. Sissy set up a frightened howl, and the two boys in the corner sprang to their feet.

'You bloody bitch!' he said. 'I'll see you in court for that!'

'Oh no, you won't! You won't risk getting near any court, when I've made my report out. And the longer you leave it before you do what I ask, the worse it'll be for you.' She took another trip to the bedroom. When she came back, her face was grave.

'It'll be too late by the time a doctor gets here, I think,' she said. 'We shall have to try to manage somehow. But I must have hot water—towels—clean sheets—proper blankets—quick. Jacky, you and your brother start breaking up those orange-boxes, quick as you can, and get that fire going. Sissy, I want you to keep the kettle boiling all the time. I suppose you've got a kettle?'

'Yes, only it leaks an' puts the fire out,' said the girl. 'Is my mam really going to die?'

'She will if you don't all help me as much as you can. Now, get that kettle on as soon as ever you can, there's a good girl.'

The girl took the kettle and began to fill it with a mug from a pail that was standing just inside the door. She scooped up the water from the little that was left in the bottom of the pail, like a child playing in its bath. The old black kettle, held in her other hand, let forth from a hole in its base a thin stream on to the floor. Dreamily the girl went on filling.

'Hurry, girl, do!' said Nurse. 'The boys have kindled the fire again already. You must hurry!'

Sissy looked up at her, with an ingratiating, simple, faraway smile.

'We're all been bit by dogs,' she said, in the tone of one simply handling out a casual scrap of interesting information.

Nurse snatched the kettle from her, tipped up the pail and poured the water into the lidless kettle.

The boys had roused the ashes and put on one or two chips of wood from the side of the hearth. Nurse plonked the kettle in the ashes, and told the boys to break up anything made of wood, and to keep the fire going all costs. With frightened glances at their father, they began to obey her.

She thrust the empty pail into Roslin's hands. 'Go fill it,' she said. 'And the bowl, and anything else that'll hold water. Then you are going down to the village, whether you like it not. I'll write a note.'

After another trip to the bedroom, she came back again, and tearing some pages from her notebook, sat down on one of the remaining boxes and took up a pencil. Whose help could she get? Time was precious, and she hardly dare risk Roslin delivering her message correctly on the telephone, even if he succeeded in getting a reply at the schoolhouse. The next telephone was at The Priory. That wouldn't do. Someone with a car could help quickest, by taking a note from her direct to the doctor. Even if he happened to be in, he would probably have to do the last bit of his journey on foot. But she had to try, however slim her chances of getting him in time were. Stavesacre was nearest, but she knew there was no one there but Margaret and the younger children. Cudweed was the next nearest place with a car. Suddenly, the calm, stalwart, homely figure of Jack Marriatt filled her mind's eye, and it seemed as if a little of the weight of the responsibility of the moment was lifted by the thought of him. She remembered him at his wife's bedside, grieving yet cheerful, strong yet gentle, busy yet always patient, burly but soft-voiced and calm, a rock of strength and hope to the very last. She had given him little thought since his wife died, but it occurred to her now that he was as likely to be at home on a Saturday evening as any man in the whole village, and he would cer-

tainly not jib at getting his car out and going for the doctor.
She began to write.

The note was a fairly long one, for she had to acquaint the
doctor with the conditions. She thrust the note into Roslin's
hands, and commanded him to deliver it personally to Mr
Marriatt at Cudweed. A shriek from the other room sent
Nurse flying to her patient; reluctantly Roslin put on his old
sacks again. He hesitated before setting out, waiting for Nurse
to reappear. When she did, he asked, a bit more humbly, what
was wrong.

'There's two babies again,' she said. 'An' the first one's
lying wrong. I'm afraid it's dead. I ought to have been here
hours ago. I might have been able to do something then. Get
off with that note, will you?'

He went. The next moment he opened the door again,
letting in a sheet of windswept rain.

'*Two* again?' he said.

She nodded. 'Perhaps even three,' she said. 'I can't be sure.'
Roslin blenched, and looked as if he were about to fall.

'Jesus Christ!' he said. 'For God's sake, Nurse, don't shake
her! She's full on 'em!' He was gone at last.

'Wake up, Sissy, now, and help me all you can. Is there any
clean rag in the house? Anything I can use for a towel? Think,
girl, think hard, and be quick.'

The girl looked round with a vacant air, smiled placidly
again and said, 'Do you know, my father thrashes my mother
with a bike tube.'

Nurse shook her in exasperation, and she cried. Then the
baby in the next room set up a wail, and Sissy went to calm
him. So much for any help Sissy might be.

It seemed to Nurse that she had never before been so cut off,
so helpless, so inadequate to deal with a situation. In all her
years of training and experience, she had never before had a
midwifery case so complicated to deal with alone, or a mother
so completely exhausted before she had arrived. Mrs Roslin
should have been in hospital hours ago, but instead of that, she

was now facing probable death in impossible conditions of isolation, poverty and unbelievable squalor. Nurse and her little black bag were all that stood between a birth and a death, and she was out in the middle of nowhere on a filthy night, with only a barmy girl and two frightened boys to help. She tried to shut out from her calculations the memory of five other children asleep in the next room. She set up the lantern to give as much light as possible, and went to work. She cleaned up her patient's face, sponging off the sweat and tears. She rebraided the beautiful ash-blonde hair, and tied it back from the face. She removed her own clean petticoat, and used it as a gown for the patient, throwing away the dirty, bloodstained dress. She took off her head square, and unfolding it, pinned it over the filthy pillow, to give the woman a clean place to turn her face into when the pains came, and selected from the pile of rags that lay on the floor the lightest and least revolting as covers. Then she prepared herself for single combat with fate and the baby so reluctant to be born. If skill and knowledge could save the mother, they should; if the first child had to die, perhaps it was the lucky one. How could such a beautiful woman ever have come to such a state as this? What chance for yet another child born into these conditions?

Almost two hours more passed in futile struggle before the sound of the outside door opening sent Nurse scurrying to see what help had come. It was the doctor. She ran to meet him and to help him off with his coat, relief flooding over her.

'How have you got here?' she asked. 'Did you get your car up? You're not very wet!'

He shook his head, turning from side to side in disbelief as he took in the scene before him.

'Good God!' he said. 'In all my years, I've never seen anything like it!' Then he answered her question.

'No—Mr Marriatt told me the road would be practically impassable by car. He went back home in his car, and then met me at the end of the road with a horse and trap. How he found

138

the way, I don't know. He says he'll wait and take us back, or go on any other errands for us.'

The door opened again, and Jack Marriatt came in, streaming rain from old oilskins and sou'wester. In his hands he held the huge gig umbrella which had sheltered them both while in the trap. They hadn't been used for years—either the trap or the umbrella, but they had served him well tonight.

Nurse was talking urgently to the doctor. 'We need sheets, towels, a kettle, bowls—there's absolutely nothing here but rags and filth. We obviously can't move her now in time. Where's her husband?'

Jack Marriatt and the doctor looked at each other. Roslin had not been passed on the road.

'Tell me quick what you want,' Marriatt said. 'My old pony's done the journey once. He'll do it again, or as many times as you need him. I dare say I can provide most of the stuff you need straight away from Cudweed. Then I'll get anything else I can from other folks in the village.'

There was no time for thanks. A list was thrust into his hands, and off he went again into the night.

Hours later, he was taking the doctor back to his car. One child had been born dead. Two others, puny boy children, lay in an orange-box, barely alive, but breathing. The mother was still under anaesthetic.

In the living-room, Sissy and the boys had dropped to sleep on the floor in the corner. It was Jack Marriatt who had kept the fire going all night, pumped and carried in clean water, and thrown out the dirty. It was he who had fed Sissy and the boys with thick ham sandwiches, cut hastily on his visit home, and plied them with hot cocoa. He seemed to have thought of everything. Sheets and blankets, towels and bundles of clean white rag: his dead wife's nightdresses and dressing-gown: a kettle, bowls, a saucepan and soap. A large can of milk, a dozen eggs, bread, cheese and thick slices of ham. Tea, sugar, cocoa and handleless cups and mugs. He had known nothing of the five other children, for in spite of all the night's happenings, they had remained asleep. It was Sissy who had asked if he had anything 'for the others', because if he had, she had better hide it, in case Dad came in and ate it all.

'Do you mean there are five more of you?' he asked incredulously. 'That makes eight, altogether?'

Sissy nodded proudly. 'Ten, now,' she said, 'an' we're all been bit by dogs!' She gazed, a faraway look in her eye, at the fire on the hearth. 'An' we're all had operations, an' all.'

The doctor having done all he could, it was left for Nurse to wait till the patient regained consciousness, and then to make her as comfortable as possible. Of Roslin there was still no sign, and Nurse was beginning to be anxious lest he should not be there to take over when she had to leave. It would not be daylight for nearly four hours yet, and though the rain had let up a little, it was still a very drear midwinter morning. Her car and council house seemed a very long way off to her. She turned to thank both doctor and farmer as they left. It was then that Jack had asked her how she was going to get back.

'I'll find my way back through the wood somehow,' she had said cheerfully. 'If that fellow does come back in time, I couldn't take him out again. He'll be needed here. I'll manage. But I wonder where he is?'

'Look, Nurse,' said Jack. 'You are just about tuckered out. I'll come back when I've got the doctor to his car, and wait till you are ready to come. Then I'll take you round by the road to pick up your car. I shan't be long.'

She protested that he also had been up all night, but the relief in her voice was obvious. She set to work again with renewed effort.

By the time Mrs Roslin was fully conscious, she had been bathed and dressed in a clean white nightdress, and when she came to she found herself in a bed properly made up with sheets, pillowcases, blankets and even an old eiderdown. The floor had been swept and cleaned, and the orange-box crib raised on blocks of wood to be level with the bed. On the other side of the bed, yet another of the ubiquitously useful orange-crates, standing on its end and covered with a tea-cloth, was doing duty as a table.

'Come on, wake up, Mrs Roslin,' said Nurse, tapping her gently on the cheek. 'Here's a lovely cup of tea for you, and two babies that will soon need your attention.'

The poor woman felt the sheets, held up her arm weakly to make sure the nightdress was real, heaved herself onto her elbow to look at her babies, and began to cry. Nurse held her and comforted her, shocked by the sudden thought that this haggard, ash-blonde girl in the bed could by age almost have been her own daughter. When the woman spoke again, there was a subtle change in her voice. The faltering words that came out were spoken in perfect English, and the tone of her voice could only called cultured.

'Thank you,' she said. 'Has the doctor gone? I wanted to thank him too. It's all the pay he'll get. It wasn't always like this, you know.'

'How you came to get in such a state, I can't believe,' said Nurse.

The girl smiled weakly. 'It just went from bad to worse, after I took up with Roslin. They turned me out from home, and I'd nowhere else to go. Now there's ten—what's to become of us I don't know.'

'Might have been eleven,' said Nurse, matter-of-factly. 'Even you can count your blessings, my girl. Now, drink up this tea, because I shall have to go as soon as Mr Marriatt comes back. You'll sleep now, after you've fed the babies. And I'll be back again by lunch time unless I've had another call. I must try to get a bit of rest myself before I go on my round.'

'Where's Sid?' asked the girl.

Nurse shook her head. 'I should think he took shelter in a hovel somewhere, and fell asleep,' she said. 'Don't you worry about him. Sissy can get you anything you need when it's daylight.'

The feeble babies, having taken a tiny feed, went back to

sleep. Their tinier dead brother, wrapped in a towel, lay among Nurse's things. She would have to dispose of that before the children found out about its presence.

When Jack came back, they roused Sissy and Jacky, and gave instructions. Then at last they left.

As the pony made its sixth trip down the slippery cart track, Jack made up his mind.

'I'm taking you back to Cudweed for a hot drink and a bit of a rest before I take you to your car,' he said

Nurse protested. 'I'm filthy. I don't know when I've ever been in such a state before.'

'You're just about done in, I can see that,' he said. 'So I'm taking charge. You can't walk to your car, so you'll have to take orders for once.'

She was suddenly so tired that she couldn't even think straight. Cudweed was one of the few places in the village that possessed the luxury of a bathroom, installed when Jack's wife was an invalid. She could think no further than that. He ran her a bath, and produced his own aged dressing-gown for her to wrap herself in. Then he went out to unharness the pony. Her dress and apron could not be worn again, and her petticoat slip had been thrown away at the cottage. Clad only in her underclothes and the dressing gown, she sank at last into the armchair near the grate in the kitchen. Then weariness and the memory of what she had left behind in the diddiki dwelling hit her, and she began to cry.

Jack was just bringing her a cup of hot, sweet, strong tea. Her tears mesmerized him, and he realized that in all the years he had known her—which must have been at least twenty—he had never before seen her as a woman, but only as the starched, brisk, efficient nurse who needed no male care or attention. The curly hair was wet from her bath and clung tightly, like a little girl's, round her face. He had an over-whelming urge to put his arms round her and comfort her. Of course he did no such thing. He merely patted her hand, and commanded her to drink up her tea. Then he busied himself about the kitchen, and when he went back to take her cup, she had put it down beside her, and was fast asleep.

He looked at the clock. It was still only about 5.30 am. He could let her sleep for an hour and a half, and still have her back at her house by daylight. Creeping lightly up the stairs, he fetched an eiderdown quilt, and covered her up. Then he sat down opposite, to wait. Before drifting off himself into a doze, he could not help the thought of how comfortable it was to see a woman again on the other side of his hearth. 'Silly old fool that I am,' he said to himself. 'Silly old fool!'

When he awoke the dawn had already broken. He roused her, and they made their preparations to leave.

'Look the other way while I put my coat on,' she laughed.

'I'll do better. I'll go and get the car,' he said. 'Leave those dishes in the sink. It's Sunday. I shall have plenty of time to do them.'

They drove through the village in the early light past cottages where lamps still burned as men prepared for work. Perce Winters had been out for a couple of hours, and was back at home eating his breakfast as they drove by. The rain had gone, and left everything washed clean and windswept. The sky was eggshell blue, so deep and clear that it looked almost transparent, and the few clouds still hanging over the eastern horizon wore pink feathers over their purple. The air was as clear and thin as wine. Jack made sure Nurse's car would start, then watched it recede into the distance. She promised to let him know the situation at the cottage after she had made her evening visit that day.

She had found the mother rested, and much improved. Both babies still held onto their frail thread of life. The rest were all enjoying a pre-Christmas feast with the food Jack had provided.

'Roslin went home about seven o'clock,' she said. 'Sissy said he got his old car started after he'd had some breakfast, and had gone out "to see a man about a dog". The whippet went with him.'

143

It was another twenty-four hours before Nurse, or anyone else, woke up to the fact that the village, and his wife and the children, had seen the last of him. The Roslins had become the communal responsibility of the village. There was much consternation about them at Stavesacre and at Cudweed. Nurse and doctor began to make representations on their behalf through official channels. Meanwhile, they had to be fed somehow. Nurse called at Cudweed most mornings, to pick up milk and eggs, and anything else Jack's good nature prompted him to provide.

From Stavesacre came the same sort of help in kind, smuggled out by Reg and delivered by Roddy, without Gwen's knowledge. It was the best that could be done for the time being, but obviously the situation would have to be resolved once Mrs Roslin was on her feet again. Reg cursed the day he had ever let a diddiki cross the gateway to his farm.

10 It's a poor heart that never rejoices

'A village is a hive of glass
Where nothing unperceived may pass'

quoted the Professor in a somewhat reproving tone to his
sister. She had been out for the afternoon, to visit Charity
Wells, and had come home full of the small bits and pieces of
news that swirl round on the surface of every village pond
every day of the year. When large events occur, like the death
of a duke, for instance, the tiny scraps disappear, only to rise
again when the waters are once more still, to move in the tiny,
intricate, interlocking patterns that in turn comprise the whole
design of village life.

The Professor was much more concerned with Virgil's
Georgics than with the bucolic pattern of the lives around him.
It was only with difficulty that he pulled himself away from
his classical meditations to utter sentences in his mother
tongue. And when he did, he was more likely to take
readymade from his store of English literature than to con-
struct phrases of his own. This irritated his sister almost beyond
bearing, because she felt he used his armoury of quotation as a
whiffler uses his sword, not for close engagement, but to ward off
any nearer approach. She didn't care what Wordsworth or Eliot

had said about life; she wanted to know what her brother thought, and said so. He defended himself by pointing out that he thought much as they thought, only they said it much better than he could.

'They have a wonderful talent for packing thought close, and rendering it portable, as Macaulay said,' he added. Selena nearly screamed. She actually lifted her umbrella, as if to bring it down on his egg-bald head. He looked up, and laughed. He had had no intention of infuriating her. The last quotation had slipped into his head, and risen to his tongue before he could stop it. He made a valiant attempt to appease her by laying down his book and pushing his spectacles up on his forehead.

'What have you heard that you think I should know about?' he asked. 'Has Miss Wells gone into a decline, or has she burnt her latest batch of Viennese fancies?'

'Really, Harold! How can you be so spiteful,' she said, but she smiled nevertheless. When they had first come to the village on her brother's early retirement, he had been the quarry in Miss Wells's manhunt, and had resigned the Viennese fancies to the last vicar's superior claims with relief bordering on the joy of a captive released from torture.

'Come now, Selena! I know you have something to report. As Fielding says, "Love and scandal are the best sweeteners of tea".'

She knew now that he was quoting deliberately, just to amuse her. She sat down and unburdened her budget.

'The new Vicar is arriving on Friday,' she said. 'Charity had it from Mrs Vernon, but Whippet Tuck told her as well. They are moving into the vicarage that day, so we shall probably see him here on Sunday. Montague Price won't like that. He's had the pulpit to himself for nearly a month. And Glenys Foreman is getting married. She's only twenty, but they say he's a very nice, sound sort of boy she's marrying. Charity heard that when she went to see Mrs Vernon about the Mothers' Union social. It seems that Glenys has chosen the very same weekend, but Miss Taylor says it doesn't matter about the school being used two evenings together. She says it's better

146

than having to clear everything up twice. They're having quite a big do at the wedding, apparently. She'll be a pretty little bride, in spite of her limp. Charity says she'll be wearing a long dress, to cover her boot and caliper up. What a good thing she's found a good husband to take care of her.'

'Then Charity went to see Mrs Jeffs, to ask her if she would sing in the choir she's training for the Mothers' Union social. Funny that Mrs Jeffs doesn't belong, though she's a member of the church, of course, and with all those children, too. She wants me to sing with them, as well—Charity, I mean, not Mrs Jeffs.' She paused for breath.

'But my dear—how do you qualify for a Mothers' Union choir?'

'Oh dear, Harold, you really are trying. You have remarked more than once about the extraordinary composition of the Mothers' Union! I don't have to join, just to help them to sing! But talking of children, there's another piece of news, though Charity says she can't vouch for it, yet. She's heard from Miss Nellie that Dr Leathers is trying to get that diddiki woman up on Stavesacre a council house. She says if old Oby Braybrooks dies, he wants that house reserved for the diddikis. But Charity says that'll cause a lot of trouble. There's several folks got their eye on that when it comes vacant.'

'Well, that's all most interesting, I'm sure,' he said, 'especially about the new Vicar's advent. He's married, I understand? Not that that will save him from unwanted attention!' He picked up his book again, and dismissed all Selena's chatter from his mind. Ten minutes later, he would have had difficulty in recalling any of it. He resembled Fletcher's character who 'breaks his fast with Aristotle, dines with Tully, takes his watering with the Muses, and sups with Livy'. It was a pity Selena was not well enough acquainted with literature to hoist him with his own petard occasionally.

In spite of Charity's prediction, it was another week before the village in general was vouchsafed a glimpse of their new Vicar. He made his way into their midst in undoubted style,

147

arriving at the church on a bright, cold afternoon in a car of so old a vintage that it excited more curiosity than he did. It was of very early post-war date, a high-slung construction of scarlet paint lined out with gold, a contraption so extraordinary that Charlie nicknamed it 'The Fire Engine' on the spot. The clergyman who descended from the ancient vehicle was as unlike the outgoing incumbent as it was possible to be, except that he too was tall. But he was thin almost to the point of emaciation, with a long, bony, ascetic face. 'Looks as if you could cut yourself on it,' was Charlie's comment. There was little warmth or humour in the deepset eyes, and the clerical garb, correct to the last detail, made his general aspect severe. True, on the occasion of his first visit to this parish, the effect was somewhat spoiled by his having to wear an overcoat against the cold wind, and the fact that he wore a wide-brimmed trilby hat; but the cleanliness of his vest and collar, and the polish of his boots below the full cassock, somehow gave warning of an equally ascetic outlook on life. The Professor, on catching sight of him, commented immediately, 'A man severe he was, and stern to view'. It was an apt quotation.

It was perhaps unfortunate that Charlie was the first to greet him. Charlie was at that moment wearing a green baize apron, and balancing on his ample stomach a crate of empties. He had been just crossing the yard with it when The Fire Engine had chugged to a standstill on the road, and he had put the crate down to go and look at such an interesting antique. He was by the side of its occupant before he understood the situation. Mrs Bluett on her way into the shop, and Martin Jeffs, one of the not too bright twins, were the only others near enough to witness the meeting.

Charlie wiped his hands on his apron, and waited for the stranger to speak first. When it became obvious that he was not going to, Charlie took the bull by the horns.

'Good morning, sir,' he said. 'I thought perhaps you might be our new Vicar. I'm glad to welcome you.' The Vicar bent a

148

regal head and replied, 'Indeed, I might. I am the new incumbent.' He did not put out his hand, and Charlie withdrew the
one he had wiped ready for a handshake.

'And who,' said the clergyman, face and tone unbending,
'might you be?' It was a form of address that smacked of
outmoded upper-class condescension, or, at least, of the
nouveau riche middle-class uppishness that was much more
difficult for an ordinary villager to take, 'born humbly and
bred hard' though he might be. It stung Charlie into most
unwonted retaliation.

'I might be King Solomon, or again I might be Dick
Turpin,' he said, 'but it just happens that I'm plain Charlie
Noble, the landlord of The Star.' He ostentatiously held out
his hand, and the Vicar reluctantly complied with a bony if
halfhearted grip, as in common courtesy bound. He then
touched his trilby to Mrs Bluett, who skedaddled across the
road like a crab to report to the other women in the shop,
keeping her gutta-percha face turned towards the newcomer
to the last.

The Rev. Lyam Costello turned his attention to the child,
who was still gawping at The Fire Engine.

'Ha, my boy! And what's your name?'

'Martin Jeffs,' (mumbled into his scarf).

'Martin Jeffs what? Eh? Martin Jeffs what?'

The boy scuffled his feet, red to the ears.

'I haven't got no more names,' he said. 'Only Martin an'
Jeffs.'

'And how old are you, Martin Jeffs?'

'Ten.'

'Ten what? Ten what?'

'Ten years'—nearly in tears of embarrassment.

'No! No, No! Ten what? Come along now, ten what?'

Martin, by now utterly confused, and wondering whether
he dared make a run for it into the safety of the cobbler's shop,
tried again.

'Ten—months?' he hazarded.

The clergyman clicked his tongue, and pulled the boy towards him.

'Martin Jeffs,' he said, 'if you are ten years old, it is quite time that you learned to address your elders with respect. The next time I ask you a question you will say "sir". Do you understand?'

The child nodded miserably. The Vicar shook him by the scarf he still held. 'Answer me properly. Do you understand?'

'Yis'—tears now ready to fall.

'Yes what? Yes WHAT?'

'Yes, I do understand. Let me go!'

He pulled himself away, and ran into Don's comforting presence to wipe his eyes on the ends of his scarf. It was perhaps even more unfortunate for the new Vicar that easy-natured, tolerant Don had witnessed the whole encounter. Don stood at the heart of the village's male society even more than Charlie, and the tale would certainly lose nothing in the telling.

Over in the shop, several women had drawn well back so as to see without being seen, and to make clear the view for Aunt Mabel from her chair in the living-room doorway. Mrs Bluett was in her element, bawling in a subdued way through a toothless orifice that excelled even its own usual geometric virtuosity.

' "Who might you be?" he asks Charlie. An' Charlie says something like he might be the King of Solomons, only he ain't. You know how old Charlie talks. Then the Vicar nods to 'im as if 'is neck were stiff an' 'e couldn't hardly bend it, an' answers. "Yes, I am the new incumbrance," he says. So that's 'ow I knowed for sure as 'e were our new man. I can't say as I like the look of 'im a lot. Too starchy, he looks.'

There was general agreement. Aunt Mabel adjusted her glasses up and down her nose, and tapped May with her stick to indicate she was to get farther out of the way and allow a clearer view. The others awaited her comment.

'There ain't no more of 'im than there is of a gutted herrin'! Looks as if he's been ate an' spewed up again.'

Mrs Bluett was quick on the uptake. 'That 'e does,' she said. 'Just like that old Jonas in the bible, what swallered a whale.'

The new Vicar's name was Lyam Costello. Miss Nellie said it must be Irish. The same thought had occurred to Charlie, when he heard it. He was discussing the matter with George Willis in the tap, when Whippet Tuck joined them. Whippet, as a good church-goer and a churchwarden to boot, stood up stoutly for the new Vicar. He had not yet had occasion to cross swords with him.

'How can he be Irish?' he asked. 'He were born in England, I know! Up north, somewhere.'

'What's that got ter do with it?' said George. 'If a dog were born in a manger, you wou'n't call it a hoss, should yer?'

There seemed to be no answer. George almost always had the last word.

Monty Price ran foul of the new parson on the third Sunday, when the Rev. Costello told him, in the vestry, that Major Bristowe would be reading the second lesson, and that in future, he, the Vicar, would be responsible for selecting other readers. In effect, Monty's services except as choir leader were being brusquely dispensed with.

The ladies who gave of their time so willingly on Saturday afternoons found that they too were liable to have their efforts inspected, changed, and on one or two early occasions, even set aside. Mrs Watson took great umbrage when she was informed that on the occasion of the Vicar's induction, his wife, who was 'a splendid organist', would be on the organ bench. Only Whippet, so far, seemed to have no cause for regret at the passing of the old, and the coming of the new.

All the same, with the time-honoured reverence for his cloth and their accustomed reluctance to find fault with one who, by virtue of his profession, stood high above them in the system, the men of the village reserved judgment, while the women went out of their way to find excuses for him. As far as they were concerned, the forthcoming Mothers' Union social would be the acid test.

The outgoing Vicar would be coming back to receive his parting gifts, and bringing his new wife to help him accept their wedding present. It would be the first occasion since the new Vicar's arrival that the village would be coming together socially, and though it was being organized by a 'churchy' institution, support would be given by a fairly wide section of the community.

Charity Wells, dismayed by the late Vicar's departure and affronted by his secrecy until he had suddenly produced a bride 'like a rabbit out of a hat', as she told Miss Nellie, took a further step backwards in spirit when it was confirmed that the new Vicar was a married man with two teenage children. She cheered up a little at the thought of the social, however, and of her own part in it. She could demonstrate to the departing clergyman what a jewel he had allowed to slip through his fingers, and at the same time show the new one that all his parishioners were not uncultured village oafs. She gave much thought to the composition of her choir. Fortunately, there were two or three besides herself and the Enrolling Member with some real knowledge of music other than hymns and songs made popular by the newcome wireless sets. But most of the rest of the ladies either bawled stridently or whispered tunelessly, especially poor old Mrs Clitheroe, the bosom friend of Mrs Watson. She had once taught the piano, and had even played the organ; but she had suddenly grown very deaf without knowing it. Consequently, she tried to sing in a key of her own choosing, and was usually half a line behind everybody else. Charity did her best to persuade the E.M. to allow her to select only those voices she wanted. The E.M. was firm. If it was to be a Mothers' Union choir, any member who wished to sing in it must be allowed to do so. Charity pinned her faith on her own ability and on the one or two good voices she could command as extras. Charity tut-tutted at the thought that one of her best assets would be Miss Nellie,

152

because though Nellie knew nothing whatsoever of it, Charity felt they were rivals. It was Nellie who suggested that Mrs Jeffs, who was known to have a fine contralto, should be asked.

'But she's Women's Institute!' Charity protested.

'So is May Quinton, but she's been asked to help with the games,' countered Nellie. Mrs Jeffs proved a willing, if somewhat irritating, convert to the cause.

'I shall enjoy belonging to a real choir again,' she said. 'I haven't sung any *good* music since I performed with the Scottish Presbyterian Singers in Halifax, Nova Scotia. We gave a splendid rendering of Stainer's Crucifixion in Toronto. It was in the year that I left Canada with my first husband to set up farming in Uruguay.'

They were to sing two batches of songs, the first with the whole choir, the second using 'selected voices', which meant she could dispense with Mrs Clitheroe's propensity to be, like the cow's tail, always behind. When introduced to the rather obscure items Charity proposed to teach them, Mrs Watson was heard to say 'Dearie me O, I thought we were going to sing songs, with real tunes, like "The Ash Grove" or "Annie Laurie" '.

'Sh!' said Charity, tapping her baton on her music-stand. 'Now, I want you to try and express in your own appearance whatever it is the words of the song are about. If the words are happy, you must *look* happy. When we sing "Greetings", you must look as if you are greeting friends, or being greeted. Do you understand? By the way you look, and stand, and by your whole appearance, you must make the audience feel what the song is about.

'Now, are we ready? Remember to look the part. If you will all stand up, we will begin with "Angels, ever bright and fair . . ." '

Where was Miss Nellie? After the practice, Charity went to the School House to inquire about her health. She found Nellie with a mouthful of pins, putting together a black sateen tunic with a white panel down the front, on which was appliquéd a bird obviously belonging to the Corvidae family. A pair of black sateen knickers, bunching out in the manner of Tudor hose, had already been made, and were lying on a chair.

'What *are* you doing?' asked Charity, as Nellie held up the tunic in front of herself and tried to measure the length.

'Oh, I'm sorry I didn't let you know I couldn't come to the choir practice. I'm afraid you'll have to do without me. Nurse has lost a lot of people from the concert party lately—mostly on account of them getting married, or having babies—the women I mean, of course. So she decided that in future it would be a good idea to have some people in it from each of her villages. I'm going to be a Magpie! Isn't that fun? At my age, too! But May Quinton has also agreed to join the concert party, and Margaret Pettigrew and that friend of hers who sings—Mary somebody or other who's come to live in that house just the other side of The Priory—her father's a new master there—and who else do you think? Mr Price from the School! It seems he's always wanted to be on the stage. And my sister's going to accompany us for the social, though she says she won't wear the costume. But she'll dress in black and white to match us for our concerted numbers.'

'I think, Nellie Taylor, that you have taken leave of your senses!' gasped Charity. 'What will the Vicar say?'

'That,' said Nellie through her pins, 'is what I'm hoping to find out. As George Willis would say, "Them as lives longest'll see most".' She kilted up her long beige wool skirt to show a pair of surprisingly shapely legs. 'Do you think the Reverend will die of apoplexy at the sight of my legs in black silk tights? What a merciful escape for us if he does!'

'It must be the change of life with her,' Charity reported later to her unmarried friend who played the violin. 'She really has gone quite foolish. I tried to reason with her, but she giggled in that silly way of hers, and said, "I'm kicking over the traces, am I? Well, well. About time too, I think".'

Coordination of the programme for the evening lay with

the Enrolling Member, Mrs Vernon. She was not happy about the inclusion of Nurse's concert party, in case they should lower the tone of the evening.

Miss Nellie was proposing a three-part programme. First, games for the children and dancing. Then the presentations, and Charity's choir, etc, followed by refreshments. Then while the refreshments were being consumed, the men would erect the platform, and the Magpies would fill the rest of the time. (Mrs Vernon winced at the thought of the concert party. It was so popular that it must be low and vulgar; but after all, if Miss Nellie and Mr Price were taking part, it could not be too degrading. Oh dear, had she not heard that May Quinton had also joined? She wished devoutly for an epidemic of scarlet fever or influenza, that would give her a legitimate excuse to cancel the whole affair.)

However, Miss Nellie ploughed on relentlessly. If the presentations were to be made from the platform, it would have to be erected before the social began at all; in which case, the amount of floor space left would be big enough for a few couples to dance, but would restrict the choice of dances, and cut out all the more popular, boisterous games.

Mrs Vernon breathed a prayer of gratitude, and decreed that the stage should be erected, and dancing only form the first part of the programme. Then Charity's full choir would sing from the platform, and the presentations made. After that Charity's friend would play her violin, and the select choir would bring the first half of the evening to a close. When the interval was over, Nurse and her Magpies would take up the rest of the time. Would Miss Nellie be good enough to explain to Mrs Quinton that her services would not now be required after all?

Aunt Mabel had made up her mind to attend the social and nothing would turn her. In vain did May point out that she wouldn't be able to stay at her side, or take her 'out the back' when required. Aunt Mabel was adamant. What's more, she needed a new frock to go in.

May sighed wearily. That meant trip after trip to town begging 'outsize shops' to let her have dresses on approval, selecting those with a sixty-inch hip and hoping that Aunt Mabel didn't inspect the label, because she insisted that she was no more than fifty-two round the behind. May met with little success at first because Aunt Mabel's taste had stopped changing some twenty years previously, and neither the material nor style of more modern fashions found favour with her. At last a dress was found that fitted in size, and *faute de mieux* Aunt Mabel had to be satisfied. She was dressed and ready to go, still complaining about the daylight robbery of asking all that money for so paltry a frock, an hour before time. It was then that she discovered a tag, sewn into the side seam, that May had failed to notice: 'Size 62 hip'. She said nothing, but her jaws worked and she rubbed thumb and first fingers together in mute signs of her rising temper. May understood that something was wrong, and sought appeasement. She really did not want a scene tonight.

She guessed that the new frock was in some way responsible for Aunt Mabel's sudden aloofness, and all the signs of an outburst.

'Your dress looks very smart,' she said. 'I must say I like the material. I'll bet it's warm, too, isn't it?'

'How should I know?' snapped the old lady. 'It don't touch me anywhere!'

'What do you mean?'

'Size sixty-two hips,' snorted Aurnt Mabel. 'I might as well take shelter in a ten-acre field!'

They set out at last, May and the children pushing Aunt Mabel's heavy wheelchair through the moon-light.

At 8.30, the previous Vicar and his wife arrived, and were effusively welcomed by Mrs Vernon and Charity, who had taken it entirely upon herself to act as the E.M.'s assistant. The new wife was by no means a beauty, but she was undeniably young—no more than thirty, against her husband's fifty and

156

Charity's own fifty-four. Then the new Vicar and his wife appeared, and the VIP party was complete.

Mrs Vernon announced that the Mothers' Union choir would sing. They filed on to the platform, everyone in her best, and formed two lines of aging, if valiant, womanhood.

Charity, clad in a flowing black dress with a cape-collar turned her back on the audience, faced her choir and tapped her baton.

'Remember—try to express the words by acting out the meaning,' she whispered.

> '*Angels, ev-er-er bright and fair,*
> *Take, O take me to thy care*'

'. . . to thy care,' echoed Mrs Clitheroe, in a different key.

The audience, seated all round the sides of the room, applauded dutifully. The choir sang on. Then Charity's friend took the platform with her violin, and proceeded to play an intricate piece of unaccompanied Bach.

'Tunin' her fiddle,' George Willis said wisely to Aunt Mabel, by whose side he had chosen to sit.

Aunt Mabel's earphone was giving her trouble. She fiddled with it till it let out several oscillating shrieks, which caused both clergymen to turn their heads and frown, while Mrs Vernon uttered a loud 'shush'.

'I can't 'ear,' said Aunt Mabel loudly. 'Sounds just a jumble o' squeaks to me.'

'Sh! Sh!' again from the chairs close to the platform, where the VIP party sat.

'I've got a new battery somewhere,' said Aunt Mabel, 'I'll put it in before she begins to play properly. I wonder where May put it? 'Old my handbag for me while I look for it, will you, George.'

The audience was now giving its whole attention to the drama of the missing battery, and conversation rose from a murmur into a rumble, as the Bach flowed on unabated. The old Vicar looked distinctly embarrassed, while the new one

157

glued his eyes to the performer, as if his ignorant parishioners could be wished away by determinedly ignoring their presence and their rudeness.

'I can't find it nowhere,' said Aunt Mabel. The violinist had reached a passage of double chords, and was displaying considerable virtuosity with her instrument, obvious only by the visual effort she was putting into it, since she could hardly now be heard above the hubbub.

George Willis leaned towards Aunt Mabel, conscious that without her aid she was almost totally deaf.

'Don't get yer bloody self excited,' he yelled. 'Feel in yer trouses pocket!'

The clapping from the front informed the audience that they had been mistaken, and they rather shamefacedly stopped their guffaws at George's wit, creating a sudden silence in which Charity was heard to say, 'Pearls before swine! That's all I can say. Pearls before swine!'

Mrs Vernon went to the performer, almost in tears.

'I do apologize,' she said. 'I am ashamed. I am ashamed.' But she had now to mount the platform, and make her speech. Her 'shame' had taken from her all remembrance of her carefully prepared speech, but she managed to extemporize fairly well and only, as far as she knew, made one bad mistake.

'I am so delighted to be able to welcome my old friend and his young wife,' she said. Nellie let out a tiny snicker of amusement, at which Mrs Vernon corrected herself hastily. 'I mean my old friend and his new wife,' she said, thereby making matters considerably worse.

But the presentations at last were made, and the speeches of thanks duly delivered. Charity's selected choir performed again to a subdued audience, and at last Mrs Vernon was able to come off the platform and take refuge in seeing that the ladies in the other room were ready with refreshments.

The audience breathed its relief, and began to enjoy itself.

After the interval, the old Vicar and his young wife having departed, chairs were drawn up to face the platform, and the

Magpies took over. Very charming they looked, too—the men in black sateen suits with white shirts, top hats and canes, and the women, from Nurse's own over-plump form to Margaret Pettigrew's slim beauty, in black tunics panelled with white over Tudor hose and black silk tights. On their heads they wore skull caps of white, winged with black feathers. Even Miss Taylor at the piano wore one of those jaunty little caps, and a white feather boa round her neck above a black dress. They were greeted with thunderous applause, and went straight into their concerted opening number.

Thereafter, a good time was truly had by all except the Enrolling Member and her party. And Charity went home in tears of disgust, taking her friend with her. The new Vicar and his wife sat on in rigid silence, disapproval reeking from them 'like steam from a dung'le' as George Willis said afterwards to Geoff Pettigrew.

By most people's standards, it was the best night out the village had had for a very long time.

It was Mrs Vernon's wont to finish Mothers' Union gatherings with prayers and a hymn, but it was the Magpies who brought this particular evening to a close with community singing, led by Mary and Monty, and accompanied by Miss Taylor at the piano, Geoff on his banjo, and Margaret with a ukelele, while the rest of the Magpies backed them with paper combs, jew's harps, and a child's drum.

Before that finale began, Mrs Vernon had slipped out, and was soon lying in a sleepless bed, crying tears of bitter chagrin, and saying over and over again to herself, 'I'm so ashamed! I'm so ashamed! What will the Vicar think?'

He conducted his first village wedding the next day, as aloof, austere and disapproving as ever.

Nurse had been invited to Glenys's wedding, but was too busy to accept. Miss Taylor had not been invited—it was understood that she could hardly attend the weddings of all her past pupils. But Nurse made it her business to be in the village at the appropriate time, and she and Miss Taylor walked up to the church together, to see the bride come out.

While the couple were signing the register, the bells rang out over the rooftops, and all the friends and relations came out of church to line the pathway from the porch.

Nurse and Miss Taylor stood at the end of the line, next to the gate, being only uninvited sightseers and well-wishers.

'Here they come!' called someone at the front, and the couple emerged to run the gamut of rice and confetti. Arriving breathless and laughing at the gate, Glenys caught sight of the two women to whom she owed so much, and stopped, dragging her husband to a standstill. Then she turned towards them, and with her free hand lifted the hem of her white wedding dress just enough to give them a glimpse of both feet clad in tiny white satin slippers.

11 Where there's a Jack

Less than a week after the social, the whole question of Christian marriage was on everybody's tongue. When the news of the king's involvement with a twice divorced American first broke, opinions rolled backwards and forwards like pebbles on the edge of an incoming tide.

Mrs Vernon's first reaction was one of relief and complete vindication of principles. All her trials and tribulations about the social were part of the church's battle against the forces of depravity let loose among the younger generation of post-war society. Now that the king himself had shown how little regard he had for the marital tie, it was time women like her arose and put their armour on. She puffed out her chest like a pouter pigeon, struck herself a blow with her own clenched fist as if testing the strength of her breastplate, and sallied forth prepared for martyrdom, if need be, in the cause of the sanctity of the marriage bond. Her first opponent would have to be May Quinton, as she was the only person in the village to whom the argument applied. Suspicion that May herself was a divorcee had always been latent, and just recently rumour had begun to clothe suspicion with substance, following an unguarded remark May had been heard to make at a Magpies rehearsal. The issue of the king and Mrs Simpson took on a much more intimate and involved nature once the whole question was linked with May and her absent husband.

In the schoolhouse, Kathleen and Nellie had one of their rare quarrels. Miss Taylor was shocked and horrified, stunned into a realization of what a constitutional crisis could do to the monarchy, and through that, to the rocks on which Britain had stood so firm for so long and become so Great. What could she tell the children?

In the bloom of her youth, many years ago, the chemist to whom she had been engaged had died of tuberculosis three weeks before the marriage. She had since felt as tied to his memory as if they had in fact been legally and physically wedded. They had loved each other in every way except for the physical union sanctioned by the ceremony. Surely 'marriage' meant something more than mere sexual union? Her view of the royal crisis was based on personal experience of a marriage made in heaven, even if heaven had seen fit to dispose of the match proposed. That any woman could commit herself twice to anything but complete, unshakeable wedlock was well nigh incredible. She thought of Glenys, married so recently, and of all her other pupils. Had she guided aright their adolescent thoughts and dreams? A teacher's job carries great responsibility.

Miss Nellie took the opposite side, completely. Was not the king seeking *exactly* the sort of marriage Kath was talking of? Everybody was liable to make mistakes. Was marriage to the wrong person the one mistake that could never be forgiven? She didn't want Mrs Simpson to be queen, but surely Mr Baldwin and the rest would deal with that? Besides, the king would eventually see where his duty lay. But she could not see why divorce should be so utterly reprehensible—as in May Quinton's case. If the man she married wouldn't live with her, was May to remain in a one-sided holy bond of matrimony with him all her life?

'It doesn't affect me, in any way,' said Nellie. 'I have never had an offer of marriage, and I'm never likely to have one

WHERE THERE'S A JACK

now. But I can quite see that if I had married the Rev. Costello in a moment of youthful absence of mind, I might now have a choice between divorce or murder.'

'Don't be so flippant!' snapped her sister. Nellie felt flippant, in more ways than one. She felt emancipated at last, and her natural capacity for making the most of small things in life sparked off a vein of flippant humour in her. She happened to be filling in a form for a small life insurance she was proposing to take out.

'It asks "state as to marriage" here! What on earth do they need to know that for, nosey things? I shan't answer properly. I shall simply write "All hope abandoned".'

Miss Taylor rose. 'Sometimes, Nellie, I think you are a case of arrested development. You never seem to get any older.'

'Thank you, Kath. What a compliment.'

'Tschk!' said Miss Taylor, but the disagreement was over. She might accept gracefully her own lot as an old maid, but it grieved her that Nellie had no memories like her own to sustain her. She suddenly realized that Nellie was the least old-maidish old maid she knew. Why did some women, like Mrs Simpson, attract all sorts of men, and Nellie none?

At Pellmell, the king's affairs occupied many a morning's gossip time.

'I blame the woman, really I do. I always blame the woman,' said Eva, over and over again. George Willis agreed with her, in principle, but found extenuating circumstances for Edward.

'You see, I reckon any chap as falls in love is like a young bullock what blunders into a cess pit. 'E's up to 'is bloody 'ocks and sinkin' afore he knows where 'e is. An' the more he struggles, the deeper 'e goes.'

'I can't understand what he can see in her, really I can't! I don't think she's very pretty, but there. Handsome is as handsome does.'

Timmy said nothing. He was in a most unusual morose mood for him. When he had been a miner, Edward, then

163

Prince of Wales, had visited his mine and stopped and spoken to him. Since that day, he had been a king's man, utterly. He was feeling personally deceived, let down and cheated. His idol had proved to have more than feet of common clay. Timmy's spirit was sapped, and he found no words adequate to describe his feelings.

The talk veered round, via May Quinton, to other cases of sexual immorality, wandering down byways of memory into the distant, pre-war past.

'Do you remember old Fanny Bradshaw?' George asked. 'She were a right 'un, an' no mistake. When she'd 'ad young Benjy (what died, you remember)—old parson Thompson went to see 'er, and tried to talk straight to 'er about 'er wicked goin's on, 'cos Benjy were the fifth child she'd 'ad out o' wedlock. She 'ad a answer for 'im, whatever he said to 'er, by all accounts.

' "I don't do it by myself," she says. "That's five on 'em I've 'ad, an' all on 'em by different men. So there's five men you can go an' call on, as well as me."

' "Why do you do it?" he asked.

' "Why do you?" she says. "If God made anythin' better, 'e kep' it fer 'isself," she says.

' "Then you admit you are a bad woman?" he says.

'She laughed, and nodded. "Ah," she says. "Put all together, I must 'av 'ad miles on it. An' I hopes God'll spare me till I've 'ad miles more."

'She were a pretty gal, an' no mistake. Married real well, in the end, I believe. Some chap come along an' took a fancy to 'er, and away the whull lot went to Australie. Got on like a 'ouse afire, once they got where nobody knowed 'em.'

The talk was back in its usual intimate channel. Only Timmy continued to brood in silence, like a dog whose master has kicked it for no reason.

The shop was less popular than usual as a meeting place, because May's presence seemed to make open expression of opinion a bit difficult. The result was that women met each other by chance in the road and stopped for a chat on the spot. Most of them were for tearing Mrs Simpson limb from limb, on the grounds that no marriage would thereafter be safe if she was given a divorce and the king married her.

'If one ain't enew, twenty's too few,' said Elsie Winters. 'If he marries her, she'll be divorcing 'im before the year's out, when somebody better, higher up, like, comes along.'

'But Mrs Winters,' said Mrs Jeffs, 'there isn't anybody higher up than the king of England!'

'That's as maybe,' said Elsie. 'She'll find somebody. Women like 'er always can. Where there's a Jack, there's a Jill.'

Mrs Jeffs left as Mrs Bluett approached. Elsie felt that the national importance of the issue justified her in having a session with Mrs Bluett, though in the ordinary way she would have passed with no more than a nod. Mrs Watson soon made up the trio.

'She must be a fascinatin' little thing, I know. Dearie me O, that she must.'

Mrs Bluett nodded wisely, stretching her mouth longitudinally to be ready to get in next.

'There were a woman as lived next door to my mother,' she trumpeted, 'as were so fascinatin', men just couldn't keep away from 'er. She 'ad thirteen child'en, an' were never married once. My mother wouldn't neighbour with 'er, never. She said it were 'er belief the woman were nothing but a common prosecutor! But I don't know if Mrs Simpson'll get her divorce, after all. I were in my neighbour's just now, and her wireless were on about it. It said the king's doctor had interfered in the case. I couldn't quite make out what it meant, but I'm sure it said something like that. An' it went on to say it might stop the degree ni-si from being made absolutely.'

Elsie Winters did not like the tone the conversation had taken. She left, and went on. Mrs Bluett and Mrs Watson put their heads close together, though Mrs Bluett was as incapable of discretion as the morning cockerels owing to her ear-shattering vocal chords. May was soon the real topic of interest. Mrs Watson, as a firm churchgoer, was denunciatory. Mrs Bluett, who liked May, stood firm in her defence.

'She's to be pitied, poor thing, that's what I say. She married beneath her sex!'

The resurgence of old rumour about her affairs neither worried nor angered May. She guessed that in Mrs Vernon's anti-divorce campaign she and Mrs Simpson were firmly bracketed together, and with cynical amusement contemplated pulling the rug from under the valiant warrior's podgy feet by simply telling the truth. When her alcoholic husband had finally become incurable, she had shouldered the burden of finding food and shelter for herself and the children.

'Talk's cheap enough,' she said, and left it at that. Uncle Bert had heard the rumour, of course, but as he was one who did know the truth, he had merely denied it. That in itself was the one thing needed to establish it as being beyond any further reasonable doubt.

Bert was the man most torn asunder by the scandal in high places. He rejoiced at the downfall of the symbol of monarchy, and waved his red flag metaphorically whenever anyone would listen. On the other hand, he argued ferociously with Aunt Mabel that it proved Edward to be 'an ordinary yuman being, just like everybody else, when it come to it'. He was very glad for him, and hoped he would be happy with Mrs Simpson as queen. Aunt Mabel was of the opinion that sins should be kept privy. Why couldn't he be like his grandfather? Uncle Bert was shocked.

'His grandfather was a most himoral man,' he declared. 'A king should know better!'

'I thought you wanted him to be like other yuman men,' said Aunt Mabel. 'You can't have it both ways.'

''E isn't no different from the rest of us,' said Uncle Bert. ' 'E's made o' flesh and blood, like the rest of us!'

'That's what I say,' said Aunt Mabel. 'He's like old Teddy. Like the rest o' you men.'

'It isn't him that wants a divorce. He's never been married. It's her. It ain't his fault she's a married woman!'

'If a gel is fit to go to bed with, she's fit to marry,' countered Aunt Mabel.

'Now then, Mabel! You wouldn't want such as 'im to be marrying just anybody, now would you? I mean to say, 'e's the king.'

'So were your great-grandfather the earl, as you make so much song and dance about. You'd ha' been keen enough on 'im marrying jus' anybody, as long as it made your grandad legitimate. I can't see why the king can't marry just as he wants to, whoever she is.'

'She can't be queen. It would upset the constitution. 'E's subject to the law of England, like the rest of us.'

'I thought you didn't believe in no laws. That's what's wrong with our country today. The king should abide by the laws what 'e's made, and marry a princess an' forsakin' all others, keeping only unter her, as long as they both shall live.'

' 'E's only made o' flesh and blood, like the rest of us. I don't believe in no kings and such trash—'

'Like a couple o' kids on a see-saw,' May remarked to Nurse, who couldn't help hearing the conversation, when she called to see May. 'As soon as one goes up, the other comes down. Then they change places to keep the game going.'

Reg stopped his car to buy some stamps. He paused on the old brick path to watch some children coming down the road, arms linked together, bawling a Christmas carol.

'Come and listen,' he said to Nurse and May, nodding his head sideways towards the children.

He held the door open for them to put their heads out, as the singing children drew abreast of the shop. Clearly their voices rang out in unison:

Hark the herald angels sing,
Mrs Simpson's pinched our king.

'That puts it in a nutshell,' said Reg. 'Drunken men and children speak the truth.'

12 God loves a cheerful giver

Christmas came with hard frost and a powdering of snow that did no more than turn the village from the workaday world to a picture on a Christmas card. Once the snow had fallen, the mid-day skies cleared to a crystalline blue from which a remote sun lit the sparkling panorama of rooftops and trees. Thatch and tile alike threw back the light in innumerable pin-points, and beneath the eaves deep pools of indigo shadow lay in wait to lengthen with the passing day. Toward sun-down, the snow-frosted branches turned pantomime-fairy pink, and the north side of the churchyard gathered the after-noon shadow together into a purple twilight as the tower caught the last pale rays of the wintry sun.

Don helped Charlie to sweep a path from the door of The Star to the road, and then in good neighbourly fashion they also cleared a path up to the shop. As darkness fell, every window gleamed gold with the glow of paraffin lamps, and paper chains crisscrossed the rooms the lamps lit up. Curtains and blinds were left undrawn and through every steamy or frost-covered window the sprays of holly and feathery ever-green, intertwined with trails of ivy, could be seen framing mirror, photograph and picture.

Old Oby Braybrooks still hung on to life, and the Roslins

still hung on to the cottage. Since Sid Roslin had taken himself off, the plight of the family he had deserted had become better rather than worse. Both Reg Pettigrew and Jack Marriatt secretly supplied them with necessities which supplemented the relief, in terms of money, Dr Leathers had been able to arrange. Jack Marriatt's gifts of vegetables and eggs and milk were not taken direct, but left with Nurse, or at the farmhouse at Cudweed for Nurse to collect before going up to the cottage. She had raided every jumble sale for miles around to find clothing for the children, and under her motherly eye the poor woman had begun to pull herself together and make the cottage more habitable. It was certainly a good deal sweeter and cleaner, and the wild, hunted look of the children at the approach of strangers was gradually leaving their eyes.

Reg Pettigrew still felt a weight of personal responsibility for their plight, though as Gwen repeatedly told him, they were no concern of his.

Reg had plans of his own for Christmas Eve, that depended on him slipping away from the house for an hour or so. He had saved three of the best rabbits from his kill, and had left them in the barn with a bag of eating apples, to take up to the cottage when he could. But he had visualized what it must be like up there in this bitter weather, and had come to the conclusion that the best gift he could bestow on the family would be a load of ready-sawn logs. There was always a huge heap of cut logs, ready for Stavesacre's own fires, left at the gate to the woods, from where one of the men fetched them as they were needed on a trailer behind the tractor. Reg had made up his mind to take the tractor up in the moonlight, load a good load of logs, and leave them outside the cottage without seeing anybody. Gwen would never know—in fact, it would be best if none of the children knew, either. Then there would be peace at home, and in his mind as well, because the Roslin children in their stable on his land would at least be warm, and even fed to satisfaction for once. The task of getting out of the house, in the event, was easily accomplished. Roddy and Margaret had

gone with friends to a dance. Angie had been lured to bed early
with promises of Father Christmas and threats of no presents if
she stayed awake to see him, while Roly had gone unwillingly
to supplement the church choir's carol-singing round the village. Only Gwen remained to notice Reg's absence, and she,
looking at the grandfather clock, remarked that she had a lot of
last minute things to do, and why in heaven's name didn't he
go down and have a drink at The Star, like other men did, out
of her way.

He had replied, as he usually did, that if he did start to go
regularly to the pub, she would complain; but as it happened,
he had to go out round the yard to make sure the cattle had
enough water, and then he had to put the tractor away. So
maybe he would go on to The Star as Christmas Eve only
came once a year.

He went out at about eight o'clock, and stood leaning over a
gate looking down at the village. The moon was nearly at the
full, and the stars burned incandescent green against the
Bristol-blueness of the luminous sky. Reflected light from the
snow gave the moon extra glory, and the night was so clear
that visibility was almost as good as in daylight. There was a
thin, keen tang in the air that stung the nose and throat as each
breath filled the lungs, making hands and face tingle as if they
had been rubbed with a rough towel. The trees stood as still as
the cottages, for there was not even a breath of wind, and the
only sounds that reached Reg as he stood there were the
shufflings of the cattle in the yard at his back, and the distant
sound of the carollers singing 'It came upon a midnight clear'.
Tears stung his eyes at the beauty of the scene, and brought
uninvited a wave of nostalgic memories, of Christmas when
he was a child; of the peak of excitement Christmas Eve
brought with it, and of his father's face in the early hours of
Christmas morning, as he looked into their bedroom on his
way down to do the milking, and asked the annual question,
'Has he been?' Of course he'd been—the bed would be strewn
with sweets and apples and oranges and toys and books, and

the mince pie and wine that had been left for him were gone. Geoff had gone 'home' for Christmas, and would be bringing his mother and father back to Stavesacre for Boxing Day. They would stay the rest of the time with Geoff in his bachelor home. Gwen did not encourage family visitors, especially since her own parents were dead. Reg sighed. Part of the magic of Christmas in his childhood had been the delight of having grandparents there to share everything. Ease of transport hadn't brought families together. It was breaking them into smaller units—like tonight. Instead of being at home, or at a sweetheart's home, helping to make toffee apples and roasting the first chestnuts of Christmas, Roddy and Margaret had gone miles away to a dance in another village. And he and Gwen were doomed to go to a ball on Boxing Night. A good excuse to ask his parents and Geoff to leave early, he thought.

Father Christmas would not call at the Roslin cottage tonight, unless he stirred himself to get on with his plan. He backed the trailer up to the gate, and filled it from the pile of frozen, snow-covered logs. Then he climbed onto the tractor, and swung out of the gate in a wide arc, coming in again to the track skirting the wood about a hundred yards from the gate. He did not want to risk getting a trailer wheel in the ditch under the hedge. He chugged on past the gap in the hedge through which the path led from wood up to cottage, and then went up the last sloping field. He took the tractor as close as he dared, and then silenced it while he threw off the logs. Then he placed the bag of apples, and a sack containing the rabbits, on the top of the woodpile, and pinned them down with some extra heavy pieces of wood. He hoped they might be found before morning, but it would not matter if they were not. The frost would keep them fresh.

Then he mounted the tractor again, and set off home by the same route as he had come, this time following the track all the way by the side of the wood.

He was under the tree, and in amongst it, before he gave it a thought. One minute he was out in the open, glorying in the moonlight and the joy of being part of it. The next, he was choked, stifled, blinded, and frozen with a drop in temperature as if he had plunged through ice into water. He was in heavy grey mist so thick it seemed utterly impenetrable, and buffeted on all sides by blows that struck like frozen cloth even while they yielded as he went straight through them. After the first moment of terror, when he had instinctively shut his eyes, he accelerated the tractor in panic, and opened them again. From every branch of the tree, so thick as to be touching each other, hung grey, translucent forms, heads down and motionless. And while the tractor bore him through them—literally through them, not merely amongst them—they bumped clammily though softly against him, and his ears were filled with the ring of childlike, frenzied laughter. Then he was out on the path again, with only the clear moonlight all round him. The whole incident could have lasted no more than twenty seconds, yet it seemed as long as a death between two lives. His hair was pushing off his cap, and the goose-pimples on his arms hurt individually as the horror pulsed through them. The deathly cold ran in shudders down his spine, and his brow was wet with beads of icy sweat. The tractor chugged on as he battled for control of himself again. Every fibre of his body urged flight, warmth, company. Every returning shred of reason urged that he turn and look behind him, either to reassure himself, or to substantiate to himself the reality of what he had experienced. Fear overcame reason for at least a hundred yards. Then he slowed up the tractor, and turned his head. The great ash tree stood out as clear in the silver light as he had seen it hundreds of times in the sunshine, just bare branches now, under the winter moon.

Then horror settled on him afresh, and he stopped no more till he was within the safety of the tractor shed. He leaned on the wall, and tried to pull himself together. He could not persuade himself that he had imagined it all. It was too real, too vivid, the memory of it too strong in all his senses. He had seen the transparent, formless forms; he had heard the childish laughter; and worst of all, he had felt them against him, though there was no substance there to feel. If he did persuade himself momentarily that he had suffered some sort of strange delusory fit, the voice of old Sammy whispered in his ear again. 'They don't call it the 'anging tree for nothing.'

He shook with the terror that still filled him, and cringed against the wall to stay his trembling limbs. After a few minutes he regained control of himself, and thought that what he needed was a good strong dose of whisky. But he could not go into the house, to where Gwen was, in this state. She would detect at once that something was amiss, and he would have to disclose the whole of his evening's doings; besides, if one word of it was ever to reach her ears, she would never stay another night at Stavesacre. He could tell no one, not even Geoff—at least, not yet. He thought of old Sam, and felt a source of support there.

At last he moved out of the shed, and walked down the road to The Star. There was a good deal of company, and it was an enormous relief to draw up to the bar among the solid human bodies, to look up to the Tudor beams decorated with multi-coloured paper chains and mistletoe, and to smell the earthy smells of burning wood mixed with beer and tobacco, and feel the taste of neat whisky on his tongue. He carried his second drink to the settle by the fire, and found himself sitting next to Sammy.

The old man eyed him keenly over the rim of his pint of beer.

'Ev'ning, Mr Pettigrew, sir,' said the old man. 'You don't look up to much, tonight. You look about like old Tom Baxter's wife did when she found a rat drownded in the cream pail.' He laughed, but kept his eyes on Reg's face.

'Ah. Only this ain't a laughing matter, Sam.' He dropped his voice. 'I reckon you are about the only one as'll understand. I went under the 'anging tree tonight, without thinking. You were right. But I don't want you to say nothing to nobody.'

Sammy nodded. 'I shan't,' he said. 'Nobody'd believe me, now, if I did. But I never told you as I'd seen nothing, did I? Or what it wa' as I see? No more will you, I reckon. Folks would only swear you'd bin drunk, an' tellin' a lot o' lies to frighten the youngsters.

'But it don't bode nobody no good, as does see it. I'm sorry it's you as is been warned; but you'll 'ev a lot o' trouble up at Stavesacre afore very long, if I don't miss my mark. It wou'n't do you no good to worry, 'cos you can never tell what sort o' sorrow's coming, nor where it's comin' from, nor how long it'll be comin'. But for them as see it, trouble's bound to come.'

'What is it, Sam? Has anybody ever give any kind of explanation?'

Sam shook his head. 'It's been called "the 'anging tree" for hundreds o' years, I believe. My old grandaddy told me about it fust, an' his grandaddy told him. People round 'ere just sort of go on remembering it, though as far as I know you're the fust to see it, except for me, in livin' memory. The only person I ever told were the Professor. I thought 'e'd laugh at me, but he didn't. He said he thought as 'ow there might all'us have been a' ash tree thereabouts, an' it might once ha' been one they 'ung sacrifices on. He said something about "the old gods", but bless you, I di'n't understand 'im more 'n half. But it appears they allus used to use a ash for their goings on in the olden days.'

'Why hasn't anybody else seen it, then? There's always plenty o' trouble goin' round?'

Sam scratched his head through his thick crop of snow-white hair.

'Well, it ain't everybody as is got the gift o' seeing. But I reckon that most folks as is ever 'eard the tale wouldn't go within a mile of it after dark, for one thing. An' if trouble comes to anybody what's bin under it an' ain't seen nothink, they don't connect the two, do yer see?'

Reg felt he must push the incident out of his mind. 'What

happened when Tom Baxter's wife found the rat in the cream?' he asked.

Sam chuckled. 'Well, do yer see, she di'n't want to lose all that cream. So she picks the rat out b' its tail, and strips the cream off it and back into the pail. Young Billy Sanders had just gone to fetch a penn'orth o' milk, an' he seed 'er do it. Nobuddy wanted her butter that week, an' she cou'n't understand it no'ow. There is them as'll swear she washed the rat in her washing-up bowl, an' poured the water back in her churn, so as not to lose no cream. But I dunno. I dunno.'

He drank contentedly. 'Made right good butter, though, Tetty Baxter did. I were sweet on her once, meself, afore she married Tom.'

He began to reminisce, mostly to himself, and Reg let him ramble on. He was grateful to the old man for sharing the experience with him, and gradually the horror of it passed off, leaving in his mind only the same sort of vague memory one has of a nightmare, once daylight has returned.

On Boxing Day, the local foxhounds met in the forecourt of The Star. Charlie was in his glory, for the sight of horse and hound linked him with the heyday of the eighteenth century, the period in history to which he felt most akin. Next, perhaps, to *Highwaymen and Robbers*, *Tom Jones* was his favourite reading matter. He could feel its atmosphere in his very bones, and persuaded himself that he was serving Fielding's robust fictional characters as he handed up the stirrup cup to the Master, and scurried round supplying the needs of all the other followers. He had unearthed from his store of antiques a set of genuine eighteenth-century pewter tankards, and had washed and rubbed them till the dull grey metal glowed with inner warmth. They would only be handed to those whom Charlie could depend upon to understand their almost tactile link with England's robust and romantic past.

As always, most of the village had turned out to see the sight and partake of a bit of extra cheer. They drank standing out in the cobbled yard, within arm's length of riders, horses, the

huntsman and his eager hounds, and they made their comments in a knowing tone put on specially for the occasion.
Uncle Bert was present, in protest against the privileges of the
idle rich. His loud remarks were highly embarrassing to his
neighbours, who tried hard to pretend they didn't know him,
and had never seen him before.

'It's a sight to make any hintelligent yuman being sick to the
bottom of 'is 'eart! If I 'ad my way, I'd 'unt every one of 'em to
death, an' let the 'ounds tear 'em to bits like they will some
poor hinnocent fox before this day's out. It ought to be forbid
by law. To think o' all them child'en being brought out just to
see 'em, as if it were a pleasant sight! Murderers, idle, fat-arsed
murderers, that's what they are.' He seemed to like the sound
of his newly coined epithet, and kept repeating it, especially
when any mounted man happened to look his way.

Major Bristowe and his children rode into the yard and
passed Bert. 'Fat-arsed, hidle murderers,' said Bert.

George Willis could stand it no longer. 'Old yer bloody
row, do,' he said. 'You go on bleatin' like a bloody old yow
wi' the megrims.'

The Jeffs family, lined against a wall, stared stolidly at the
Bristowes. Their mother remarked, in a loud tone, what a
good seat The Major had. 'Just like my dear first husband—
your own father, Roy. He had a wonderful seat. I remember
when he took the Prince out riding on the pampas' . . . Her
voice was drowned in sudden hubbub. One of the hounds had
taken exception to the presence of Roddy Pettigrew's pet cat.
The fracas was only silenced by Roddy buttoning the spitting
feline safely inside his leather coat, and moving farther away.

Margie was there, drinking a half-pint of ale in full view of
everybody, tossing her ginger curls provocatively at anything
in trousers or breeches. A fine-looking girl she was, too, as
many a man privately thought. She sat perched on the arm of
one of the benches round the pump, literally at the centre of
the colourful scene. The Master raised his quirt in her
direction—a gesture of recognition that did not go unnoticed,

especially by the other women present. She had no fear of horses (or of anything else on legs for that matter) and put up her hand to stroke the muzzle of any horse within arm's length.

'Showin' her wares off, bold as brass! Set her stall out proper, an' no mistake,' Mrs Watson reported afterwards to the chairbound invalids at Pellmell. 'Got a buyer, an' all, from what I could see. O yes, dearie me O!'

'Really? Who? One o' the gentry?'

'No, though she wasn't losing no chances wi' them, I can tell you. No, the one as couldn't take 'is eyes off her were Maudie Tuck's husband. It seems that as soon as ever they got to Old Martha's for Christmas, he asked where the nearest pub was, an' off he goes down to The Star, on Christmas Eve. He's a Welshman, ain't he? Morgan Evans, they say his name is—but it seems they call him Mog, for short. Anyway, he must like his pint better than 'e likes Maudie's company, or her mother's. Been down at The Star every minute 'e could over Christmas, 'an gone 'ome drunk as a lord every night, according to some. Margie's been down there at The Star, playin' the piano for 'em, and it seems this 'ere Mog's bin singing with 'er. Got a beautiful voice, Whippet says, but he wouldn't go to church, on account of all Welsh folk being chapel. I asked Whippet if 'e went to chapel then, but Whippet only laughed an' said he reckoned a pub were as near to church or chapel as Mog ever got. You can see Whippet don't take to 'im much. It ain't to be expected though, really, is it? Him being a foreigner as they didn't know when Maudie took an' married him. Anyway, I've heard as there's been terrible rows up at Martha's all over Christmas, on account of him being at the pub all the while. Seems to me as Margie were the attraction more than the beer. But I dunno, dearie me O, that I don't. I dunno what the village is coming to.'

Certainly the handsome Welsh stranger was paying attention to Margie on the morning of the meet, though it was only to replenish her glass beneath his wife's suspicious eye. There was a big family of Tucks between Whippet and Maudie.

178

Whippet had been born before Martha had married, and was in fact Tuck only by village courtesy. Maudie had been an afterthought, 'born in the change, and one of a twin,' as Martha would explain, *sotto voce*, to anyone interested. Maudie had been petted and pampered, and was of a fiery disposition. She was certainly not one to brook rivalry or play second fiddle. Mrs Watson had noted the beginnings of an interesting situation.

The horses getting restless, the Master looked at his watch. The noise died down a bit, in a sort of anticipatory silence.

'Of course, you hunt tigers on elephant back,' sounded Mrs Jeffs' voice across the yard.

The hunt moved off, stringing out down the village street to the music of commands from the huntsman to his hounds, and the jingle of bridle and bit. Somehow, the day was suddenly empty and flat without them.

'Fat-arsed murderers,' said Uncle Bert into the air, as a Parthian shot.

'Just a little dull, compared with the rodeo's I used to take part in in Calgary,' Mrs Jeffs opined to May.

13 There's two sides to every question

The first surprise of the New Year was that Maudie and her husband did not return whence they had come. They stayed on with Old Martha. Mog did not seem to have a job to return to, though he always seemed to have plenty of money. After the first few weeks, however, he brought home one day a small two-seater car, and from that time on he worked at a garage on the outskirts of the town, while Maudie dropped back into her old place in Martha's cottage.

There was an uneasy peace there, as there was at Stavesacre. The news that Rose Townsend was expecting again caused a momentary stir, but was soon exhausted as a topic. After all, everyone had expected that she would be expecting before long. They all expected a boy, this time, confidently predicting the result they all wished for, in effect. Change was the thing they feared more than anything else. A son up at Dindle would give them all a settled sense of security again.

Then, at the end of February, Oby Braybrook fell out of bed and rolled in front of the fire his neighbours kept burning in his bedroom, which was in fact the living-room of the council house he occupied. It was Mrs Bluett who found him when she called to take him his old-age pension. She pulled him away from the fire and ran out into the lane to get help. George

Willis happened to be passing, and went back with her, leaving his horse and cart to stand. Then he came running out again, and went down to the schoolhouse as fast as he could. Miss Taylor was in school, but Miss Nellie opened the door to his knocks.

'Phone for the doctor, will you?' he said. 'For poor old Oby. He's done for at last.'

Nellie took the receiver from its hook on the wall just inside the front door, motioning George to step inside. He stood beside her, holding his cap in his hands, while she asked the operator for the doctor's number.

'What shall I tell him?' she asked George, as she waited.

'He's fell out o' bed.'

The doctor was at home, and answered quickly. Nellie gave the message. She turned to George, her hand over the mouthpiece.

'Dr Leathers says he's very busy, and wants to know what Mr Braybrook's injuries are. He can't come just because the old man's fallen out of bed, if he isn't badly hurt. What's he done?'

George's face was a study. It was always red, by nature and weathering. It now took on a tinge of mouldy-beetroot purple, and his neck swelled with embarrassment. He ruffled his dark hair with the hand that held the cap, and then took the hand down again to hold the cap in front of him as if to cover his own nakedness. Then he pulled his moustaches down at each side with his other hand, while he searched for words in which to convey to this delicate maiden lady the information the doctor required. Even his normal, gore-laced vocabulary seemed to have deserted him, and no utterance suitable at all for a lady's ears would rise to his tongue.

The doctor was getting impatient. 'Put George on the 'phone, for God's sake,' he ordered Nellie. She strove to obey the command. George turned from purple to green.

'No—no—I ain't goin' to 'andle one o' them bloody things,' he said, backing away from the 'phone. 'They ain't for the likes o' me. You tell 'im!'

181

'Tell him *what*?' said Nellie. 'I can't tell him unless you tell me, can I?'

George, cornered, took the plunge, 'Tell him,' he bawled, as if Nellie were at the other end of the line instead of a foot away from him, 'Tell 'im as 'e's very near burnt 'is bloody arse off, an' fried his bloody onions an' all.'

'It seems,' translated Nellie, struggling with the giggles that rose in her throat in spite of the horror of the information, 'that he has sustained some injuries to his private parts.'

'I heard,' said the doctor. 'Tell George I'm on my way.' He could only pack the poor old man off to hospital, where he died two days later from shock. The topic of his death had hardly been touched on by the knots of gossip vendors, before it was displaced by its sequel. The Roslin family had been awarded the tenancy of his house, and would be moved in as soon as the old man's few sticks had been cleared out. At every social level below that of the professionals and the farmers, the reaction was violently against this move. It was violation of the very worst kind of the community's corporate identity, and they came together into a solid block of antipathy towards the diddiki family. It was as if the doctor, whom they had trusted, had placed a nest of vipers in their bosom.

'Bad'll become of it,' said Elsie Winters, and few disagreed with her.

The first outward sign of trouble came when March brought with it the annual parish meeting. The village was too small to qualify for a parish council properly elected, though Alastair Lewis, Uncle Bert's lugubrious communist friend, had for a long time been agitating to get it upgraded. The parish meeting required only two officers, the chairman and the secretary. By tradition, the chairman was the Vicar. The secretary's job had passed from hand to hand a bit, but the truth was that nobody wanted the thankless task that had all the work (such as there was) and little power. Charlie, under duress, had taken it on one year; and the Professor had been coerced into it another year; but as the latter had completely forgotten he was supposed to be taking notes for the minutes, and had followed the trails of any red herrings thrown up at the meeting far back into antiquity in his thoughts instead of minding what was being said and done in his sight and hearing, he had proved a dead loss. Women were by tradition left out of consideration, and few others were educated enough to string the minutes together. Farmers and professionals alike pleaded the weight of other demands upon their time. By a process of elimination, the lot had last year fallen on Alastair Lewis. The departed Vicar, in the chair, had been warm in Mr Lewis's praise, and it was true that they had rarely had so competent and well-informed a secretary. He was pretty sure of being re-elected, but it irritated him almost beyond bearing that the establishment should have the real control of the only bit of theoretical democracy village life boasted, and he wanted the chair for himself. That in fact the real meaning of democracy was being demonstrated all the time in the village he did not recognize, since in theory democracy could not cohabit with the hierarchical system in practice.

The meeting was due to begin at 7.30 pm in the schoolroom. They sat at the dual desks, and on infant chairs brought hurriedly in from the next classroom. The men at the back sat uneasily on top of the desks, backs against the wall charts stuck insecurely against the shiny brown paint of the dado, and heads in front of the examples of children's work mounted even less securely on the cream paint above it. The slightly musty smell compounded of child (especially wet child), drying clothes, ancient paper, fresh glue, the cheap brand of special school ink, disinfectant and above all old wood, was made even more nostalgic after dark, when the swinging oil-lamps, suspended from the high vaulted ceiling far above, had been lit in the big room. They gave out a pungent smell of paraffin, and more than one memory was stirred by the aroma, to recall the very few exciting occasions in their childhood when they had ever seen the hanging lamps lit.

Miss Taylor's presence inhibited most of the indigenous.

She embodied authority for those who had sat in this room under the stern eye of former 'governesses'. Some of those present had indeed been her own pupils. Talk was conducted in whispers, and shuffling kept to a minimum.

The room was stuffed to overflowing as it had never been before. At 8 pm they were still awaiting the arrival of the Rev. Lyam Costello. At 8.15, Lewis rose and brought the meeting to order.

'I must point out that the new Vicar has not been elected chairman of this meeting,' he said. 'If he were present, we should still have to vote him into the chair. As he is not, we must proceed without him, and elect a new chairman. Is anyone willing to stand?'

Everybody looked at everybody else. Whispers went on between the farmers present, but every head was resolutely shaken. Some looked towards the Professor, but he was too far away in spirit to reach, having been brought to the meeting against his will by Selena. Eyebrows were raised towards Charlie, but he endeavoured not to see them. Feeling their pressure on him beginning to tell, however, he squirmed and sought an escape route. Sitting in isolation at the back was Major Bristowe. Charlie rose and proposed him as Chairman.

If looks could have killed, Charlie would have died on the spot as the daggers in the incredulous eyes of his neighbours struck home. The utter silence that followed his proposal was nothing to that which ensued after Lewis's request for a seconder. The dogged embarrassment of all present was painful. Bristowe was just about to decline the honour when Uncle Bert's voice cut across the stillness, proposing Mr Lewis himself.

'I second that,' said a Welsh voice from the back row. Heads turned as one, at the sound of this new piece of effrontery. A self-confessed communist was being voted into the chair by a foreigner. They were flabbergasted, unnerved, bereft of reason and of voice.

'All in favour?' said Alastair. 'Any against? Thank you!' It was done, while they, in stupefied silence, had allowed it to happen. The next moment, Bert had been made the new secretary—proposed from the chair (probably illegally), seconded again by Mog Evans, and allowed to stand because everyone else was too courteous to make the loud protest they would certainly make once they got outside.

It turned out to be an interesting meeting. For one thing Alastair Lewis had been doing his homework on the chance of being able to show his ability. All the usual formalities and annual topics were soon dealt with, efficiently and correctly—even the accounts of the Wootton Charity seemed to be in order. Whippet Tuck and young Jim Woodward of Pellmell (in their role of churchwardens being *ex officio* trustees of the charity) explained that they had sought last year permission to distribute cash instead of red flannel to those entitled to benefit—red flannel no longer being acceptable, for one thing, and so costly now that each old lady would have received only approximately a quarter of a yard. In the same way, each old man could have had nothing more than bootlaces instead of boots. They had therefore doled out half-a-crown all round to those members of the community over seventy-five years of age who were members of the Anglican church.

The new chairman said he had been studying the trust, out of pure interest. Were the trustees certain that they had interpreted the bequest correctly? Were not chapel people also eligible? (Murmurings of dissent all round, even from chapel folk.)

Mrs Vernon rose from her seat, swelling at the chest like the frog in the fable. To the best of her belief she said, this was not a matter for the Parish Meeting at all, but for the Vestry Meeting. It was entirely a church affair, which in the past had been dealt with by the Vicar at the Parish Meeting simply in order that justice should be seen to be done. But the wishes of the benefactor, and the conditions of the trust, must be adhered to. She was sure it stated unequivocally that those

185

eligible should be 'members of Christe's bodie in ye churche'. Was not that clear enough?

'Do you happen to know the date of the bequest, Madam?' asked the chairman.

'No, Mr Chairman, I do not. But I know it to be of great antiquity, and I stand here firm to see that no encroachments are made upon it by those of other denominations, or those of no denomination at all.' She glared at him, and struck the side of her ample chest with her clenched hand, at which her hidden breastplate of whalebone gave out a comforting response of tough, unyielding sound.

'The date of the Wootton Charity, according to my information, is AD 1472. That was before the Reformation, madam. "A member of Christe's bodie in ye churche" at that time would have been anyone who had been baptized a Christian. I beg to give notice that if I should live to be seventy-five years of age, I shall demand my rights to my share of this charity. Though I have no belief whatsoever now, I can prove that I was baptized a Christian, and made thereby 'a member of Christ'. I shall fight the matter in the courts, if need be; but I shall have my rights.'

The babel of voices that followed this declaration sounded more like a Helping-Hand-Club Outing returning in the early hours than a sober Parish Meeting in session. Tongues that half an hour before had refused to function to prevent a man they disliked being made chairman, now refused to be silenced by his repeated shouts of 'Order! Order!' and Bert's attempt to support him by banging on the teacher's desk with the minute book. There was no longer solidarity in the will of the people. Church people were adamant in their exclusive right to half-a-crown's worth of red flannel when they should be seventy-five years old. Chapel people could only rage indignantly at having been done down by the Vicar and churchwardens all those previous years. Only Miss Taylor asked to have the relevant parts of the trust deed read out, and she couldn't be heard, in spite of the fact that she reached instinctively for her handbell, and rang it lustily. It caused only a momentary pause in the hubbub, in which the Professor's voice was heard shouting, at the top of its pitch, into George Willis's ear: 'Henry the Eighth—wanted to divorce his wife.'

'I thought his name were Edward the Eighth!' (From Sally Watts's husband Wilfred who happened to be sitting next to George.)

'Bugger it, they're all alike mate seemingly.' (George Willis to Wilfred Watts.)

'Sh! Ladies present.' (Luke Townsend.)

'Order! Order!' Bang! Slap! Miss Taylor's red inkwell spat red ink onto the chairman's papers.

Pandemonium broke out afresh, not to be quelled until Mrs Jeffs proposed that the matter be referred back until some investigation into the legal position of the charity could be carried out. Whippet Tuck sat down, wiping his brow. The meeting rumbled darkly, like thunder over the horizon.

No one could remember a meeting before at which anybody had ever expressed any opinion forcefully. The dragon of democracy's chains had certainly been loosed by the new people at the teacher's desk.

'Cry havoc! and let slip the dogs of war,' said the Professor to Selina, his attention having been recalled by the noise, and his interest now thoroughly roused.

'Sh!' said his sister. 'I want to hear what's happening.'

Next came the question of electing someone to serve as the Meeting's representative on the Board of Managers of the School. Charity Wells on her feet, this time, saying in her throaty voice that the vicar had always served them well in this capacity. Mrs Vernon, anxious to back Charity, said:

'There can be no question, of course. The Vicar is *ex officio* the parish's representative on the managers.' Miss Taylor rang her bell again, and got the silence she intended.

'I'm sorry to contradict Mrs Vernon, but that statement is not correct. In previous years, we have simply been asked to endorse the proposal that the elected representative be asked to

187

carry on. It just happens to have been the vicar for a considerable time. But it is not an *ex-officio* appointment. Anyone here
could be appointed.'

Normally, Miss Taylor never raised her voice, on principle,
at the Parish Meeting; but the temptation to prove herself in
the right as far as the Rev. Costello was concerned was too
strong for her, and over-rode her common sense, because a
difficult villager on her controlling board of managers was the
last thing in the world she wanted.

Confusion looked like breaking out again. The chairman
once more took charge, and asked for nominations.

'I think it should be a parent,' called out Mrs Jeffs. (Miss
Taylor looked utterly appalled, a fact Miss Nellie noted with
some unsisterly satisfaction.) Nobody proposed Mrs Jeffs.

'I propose the Vicar,' said Mrs Vernon. 'After all, he is a
parent.'

'I think the chapel should have a say in it,' said Luke
Townsend. 'It is a council school after all, not a church
school.'

Nobody proposed Luke Townsend. Mr Lewis desired that
nomination for himself. Equally, he wanted to be a good
chairman, and the Vicar had so far been the only proposal. Wit
came to his aid.

'We can hardly appoint the Vicar in his absence. He might
not wish to stand, after all.'

Miss Taylor suddenly saw the pit she had dug for herself.
What would life be like for her with that dour-faced, politi-
cally minded creature on the board of managers of her school?
The other managers, all appointed by the LEA, were aged
'county-type' folk who were content to let well alone by
instinct and experience, and refrained from interfering in matters which they did not understand. Miss Nellie read her
sister's face accurately, and followed her train of thought. She
plunged in to avert disaster.

'I propose Mr George Willis,' she said clearly above the
gathering murmur.

'I second that!' said Charlie.

'Any other nominations?' disappointedly from the chair.

'I propose Major Bristowe.' (Mrs Vernon.)

'I second that, if the Major is prepared to stand.' (Charity Wells.)

The Major graciously let it be known that he would be so willing. A vote must be taken. George Willis was trying to make it known that he was not willing, but Miss Nellie, in league with Charlie and the Professor, managed to silence him. Miss Taylor provided paper and pencils, and Bert, assisted by Mrs Jeffs, went into 'the little room' to count the votes. Meanwhile, the chairman arranged the date of the next meeting, a year ahead, and asked, 'Any other business?'

It was by this time past 9.30 pm and people had already begun to gather their belongings together, with anxious glances at the school clock on the wall.

There was other business, apparently. Major Bristowe had reasons of his own for being there at all, and for staying on to the end especially after the snub he had received. He rose to request that footpaths and bridle paths that crossed his fields and pheasant preserves at Campion's Hall should be deleted from the parish map (if they had not been used regularly in living memory), or at least diverted to the side of arable fields. This was necessary to prevent the new brand of hiker from the town destroying standing crops.

The meeting was split asunder again, in an entirely different way from the first time. It was now a 'them' versus 'us' situation. Every farmer and smallholder stood shoulder to shoulder behind Bristowe. The workmen and their wives, however, were aghast at the proposal, and they were backed by all the romantically minded—Charlie, Miss Taylor and Nellie, and the Professor—though in retrospect none of these could remember ever having walked a footpath on the Campion's Hall fields. They—the labourers—were being robbed of ancient rights, and would have none of it, even though when challenged few of them knew where a single genuine public foot or bridle path existed. They made wild claims with regard to any short cuts they were in the habit of using to and from work, church or pub, and denied strenuously any map reference that crossed their gardens or allotments. After half an hour's wrangling, this matter was also referred for investigation. Then Mrs Jeffs handed the result of the ballot to Mr Lewis, who cleared his throat and announced that by a clear majority Mr George Willis was the new school manager. That worthy beamed with gratified unbelief, his eyebrows pointing heavenward to show his incredulity, while he clapped his cap again and again over his upraised, bent knee. Major Bristowe left, during this demonstration of his victorious rival's pleasure, to the tune of George's voice saying again and again, 'Well, I'll be buggered! As I go to school!'—which remark, as Nellie said afterwards, was hardly to be taken at its face value.

'Any other business?' said the lugubrious chairman once again, and again there was a stirring of the waters in the back benches.

'Go on—get up and say it,' somebody was being urged, in frantic whispers.

'On your feet, boyo,' said Mog, in sibilant encouragement. Everyone turned to stare, and at last there struggled to his feet Sonny Tuck, Maudie's twin brother.

A small man, Sonny was as timid and inoffensive as Maudie was pert and precocious.

'I want to know, sir,' he said, choking back gulps and near tears of embarrassment, 'how it is as diddikis can get an 'ouse when us in the village as wants an 'ouse can't get an 'ouse.' Murmurs of agreement from all except Reg Pettigrew and Jack Marriatt.

'I bin wanting an 'ouse ever since I got married. I hadn't got an 'ouse then so I had to go an' live with my mother. Then our Maudie got married, an' she hadn't got an 'ouse neither, so she come home as well. There ain't room for us all with Mother. I got to 'ave an 'ouse. If I don't 'ave an 'ouse soon, my wife says she shall leave me for somebody as 'as got an 'ouse. I don't want her to leave me just 'cos I can't get an 'ouse, when diddikis as come from nowhere and don't belong to us can get an 'ouse without askin' for it. I want an 'ouse. I thought as I should get Old Oby's 'ouse when he died, but I didn't. I want to know why I can't 'ave an 'ouse . . .' he broke down, in actual tears of frustration, anxiety, and embarrassment.

'Dear, oh dear!' was heard on all sides. 'It's not right, though, is it?' 'Born an' bred here, he was, and his family afore him.' 'Ah, right back to the time o' Robin Hood. Parson Williams told me so.' Whippet was backing his younger brother for once.

Alastair Lewis rose majestically, once more calling for order. The matter was indeed right up his street, but he was tired now, and a bit disturbed; besides, he was not at all sure which side of the argument he ought to take.

'I'm afraid I can't deal with such a large question under "any other business",' he said. 'I therefore declare the meeting closed.'

Poor Sonny, absolutely drained by his heroic effort to put forward his own case, was still wiping away his tears, and even Mog made no further protest. The extraordinary meeting suddenly fizzled out like a match in a roadside puddle, and its members dispersed and scurried home like field mice in the shadow of the barn-owl's wings.

'Whew! What a meeting!' said Nellie to herself as she shot upstairs to avoid any recriminations from her sister with regard to the new school manager. 'It's stirred up a real old hornet's nest, specially if poor Sonny has to wait another whole year before he gets 'an 'ouse.'

The old order might indeed be changing, but it would still be a long time before the will of the people supported anything new and untried.

'They're a hignorant lot,' Bert opined to May, as they walked home together. What they believe is "All yours is mine, but all mine's my own".'

'That applies to most folks, whatever they call themselves on Sundays and election days. There's a couple I could name that it fits real well.'

She left him. He rarely had the last word, either with May or Aunt Mabel. Women, he thought bitterly, never could follow an argument through without getting personal about it. Yet there were those who said the day would come when a woman would be Prime Minister! Bert comforted himself with the thought that 'the people' wouldn't stand for that. A truly democratic election would put a stop to all that nonsense.

14 The rotten stick cracks first

The everlasting miracle of spring was behind them again, and hard work, combined with routine happenings, carried them through the months of early summer. 'Come day, go day, God send Sunday,' said Mrs Watson, tossing her head to indicate the deplorable lack of events to talk about. Luke Townsend's wife produced a boy, as desired, and named him John Mark. Maudie and Mog stayed on, and Sonny's wife went home, temporarily, to mother in the next village. The Roslin family were installed in the vacant council house, and Nurse worked extra hard to coax bits of unwanted furniture for them from people in her district who knew of the situation only by hearsay. Miss Taylor suffered an influx of five new pupils who had never before set foot in school, and had no intention of staying there if escape were possible. She despaired of getting the older ones to read or write, and concentrated on trying to make them reasonably at ease among their fellows, a hard task since none of their fellows appeared willing to cooperate. She and Nurse between them endeavoured to inculcate ideas of hygiene, especially with regard to headlice. The Roslin children could be, and were, blamed for everything from nits to ringworm, from impetigo to whooping cough.

It seemed that Nurse's old bike, as well as her car, were seen in and about the village three or four times now for every once in the past. Of course, some of her visits were social ones, as The Magpies continued to flourish in its new form, and plans had to be made ready for the next autumn season. Eddie Linsell was gaining a growing reputation as a preacher, and now spent every Sunday in the pulpit, taking three services and a prayer meeting quite often on the day appointed for rest, and covering miles and miles between chapels on his second-hand cycle. Monty Price still went somewhere on Saturday mornings, but since he had been included in The Magpies he had ceased somewhat to be the enigma that had previously kept interest in his doings alive.

The Vicar had made gradual alterations that deprived Monty of his role as second-in-command, and it was now the Major who read the second lesson as of right. In fact, one of the few remarkable things of this spring and summer was the growing intimacy of the Vicar's family with that at Campion's Hall. News was brought that the Vicar had been seen on horseback with the Major, looking as if he had been born to the saddle, and obviously enjoying himself. This proof that he was truly human was greeted with a fair degree of satisfaction, and very few adverse comments. They were growing accustomed to his austere face, and sought to endure with good grace a situation it was not in their power to cure. Little by little, the details about him and his background began to seep out and percolate his parishes. His father was a baronet; he was an author who had published books on the West Indies; his wife was the daughter of a famous violinist; she had money of her own; he would be a very wealthy man when his mother died, although he would not get the title, which would go to his elder brother, along with all the family estates. The fortune would come from his maternal grandfather, who had left a huge sum in trust for him until such time as his mother had no use for the interest on the invested capital.

All this tended to place him higher in the estimation of his parishioners than his cold personality had previously seemed to warrant. If they could not like him, at least they could be proud of his exalted status, and at the same time make excuses for his being as he was. Since the death of the Duke, they had regretted the loss of their lifelong connection with the aristocracy. Though the Vicar was only on the fringe, compared with the Duke, the general feeling was that half a loaf was better than no bread at all, and that his birth had somehow redeemed some of his shortcomings as a country parson. Strangely, he had found a champion in Charlie. After the meet on Boxing Day, The Fire Engine had chugged into the yard of The Star one day, and the Vicar had requested to see the pewter tankards he had heard had been in use at the meet. Charlie had taken him into his stables, and they had had a fascinating hour together, for it seemed the Vicar was an antique lover and collector in his own right, and very knowledgeable into the bargain. They had parted with mutual esteem much increased.

Late in the summer, it was rumoured that the Vicar's mother had died. Later still, the grapevine reported the possibility of a curate to assist the Vicar. He was finding his work too much for him, especially as one of his parishes had been suddenly increased in population with the building of a large new estate by a local speculative builder. New schools were envisaged, together with other new amenities that would draw even more people in. In July, the curate became a reality. If hearts beat quicker among the maiden ladies, it was not long before the sight of the curate in the flesh dashed all hopes and dreams again. True, he was still unmarried, but that was probably because he was still young—no more than twenty-five or twenty-six. And he did not, on the surface, seem to fit into any of the categories of parson to which they were accustomed. He was tall, well-muscled, and undeniably handsome. He was an excellent all-rounder with regard to sport, but preferred rugger to any other game. He delighted the Professor by his intimate knowledge of the classics, and his willingness to talk about books in general. He joined Miss Taylor and her class one day when they were out for a nature walk, and turned a dull routine lesson into a memorable botanic occasion. When they collapsed to rest by the side of a brook, he lay flat on his back and told the children stories until Miss Taylor withdrew to sit on a tree stump, and left him to cope with the children alone. When he rose at last, his head was crowned with daisies, and wreaths of meadow flowers hung about his neck. Miss Nellie, watching from the schoolhouse window, noted that he did not remove them, even when the children returned in a formal crocodile to school with their teacher and her uninvited assistant at the head of it. He strolled into the bar of The Star and was as much at ease with a pint of ale in his hand there as he was chatting over a cup of tea with Martha or with Aunt Mabel.

He was, in fact, a thoroughly unspoilt, uninhibited, unselfconscious, strong, healthy, happy and contented specimen of British manhood, so far unattached and fancy free. He came from a clerical family and his call to the priesthood was utterly genuine; but like the rest of his family, he was a thinking man first, and a reluctant upholder of doctrinal decisiveness second.

He had been at a loose end, work-wise, when one of his father's friends had recommended him to the Vicar as an energetic youngster who wouldn't mind pushing a bike from one village to another on Sunday mornings, or taking confirmation classes in draughty church halls on winter evenings. His arrival had been arranged to coincide with the holiday season, in order that he might be well installed before the Vicar and his family left for a summer vacation. As it turned out, he arrived only twenty-four hours before the Vicar was called away to his dying mother's bedside, and the two men had had the minimum of contact before the foreplanned holiday had left the young curate virtually in charge. His freshness and vigour had captured the hearts and the imagination of the parishioners before the month was up. A few, like Miss

Taylor and Nellie, pondered on the clash of personalities that must arise when the Vicar returned, and looked into the future with some foreboding. A few, like Mrs Vernon and Charity, regarded the new curate with distaste as being *avant garde* in his thinking, and obviously not of the same high class as the Vicar; some found his hearty enjoyment of life incompatible with the dignity they expected of the cloth, and some distrusted the ease with which he adapted himself to any company he chanced to find himself in. Elsie Winters was one who 'didn't take to him'.

'He's too sweet to be wholesome—like a 'tater that's been friz,' she said. But Mrs Bluett spoke loudly in his praise as one who 'clashes with every word you say'. George Willis said sagely that new brooms always swept clean, and Whippet Tuck agreed that only time would tell.

It was the end of August when the Vicar returned. Two days later, he picked up a letter lying on his sideplate at breakfast time, and opened it.

Dear Sir,
   When the cats away the mice do play i think you did not ought to go off and leave your work to somebody what is not suitable. there is things going on here as you would not beleive and you did ought to no about and if you are on your hollidays how can you i mean your new Curate as is to young to be a proper parson even if he was rite in his head which i for one do not think going about drest in daisychains and wasting his time playing with children as ought to be doing there lessons proper in school. besides he does not behave hisself like a parson drinking in the pub mixing with them chapel folks it is a disgrace and somebody will have to do something about it and i could tell you a lot more about what goes on in this place who think nobody knows about there goings on people as belong to your church and them as is looked up to on account of them suppose to be kind but i see her with my own eyes in his house in nothing on only a pair of underlinen what was she

197

doing there at five oclock in the morning where had she been all night i should like to no when respectable folk is abed them as lives longest will see most but i no now and so do you and it will have to stop

from

a well wisher.

The Vicar dropped the letter from his fingers onto the table. His first instinct was to crush it in his long lean-fingered fist and send it in disgust to the wastepaper basket. Like most of his class, he regarded the anonymous letter and its writer as wholly beneath contempt. The only thing to do with such filthy things was to ignore them completely, as the only way to deal with blackmail was to go straight to the police. His theories on such happenings had been worked out long ago, and he was quite sure where he stood on such matters. But in all his fifty-odd years till now, he had dealt only with hypothetical cases.

He checked his hand in the very act of crushing the paper, spread out the letter and in spite of himself read it again. He must burn it, of course, not leave it where the cleaning woman could possibly find it. He tucked it into the inside pocket of his jacket and looked round for the envelope, which of course must be destroyed as well. The envelope was addressed in an uneven, uneducated hand of block capitals printed in pencil, though the letter was in a cursive hand and written in ink with a pin-point nib that had caused several blots and smudges. In spite of himself, he was beginning to follow clues and to wonder about the identity of the writer. The postmark was quite clear—it had been posted the previous afternoon in May Quinton's post office. That settled which of his villages it referred to. Or did it? Would not someone who wished to cover any traces of his or her identity deliberately post his dirty communication somewhere other than his own place of residence? By the same token, would not an educated person choose to make it appear that he was something other than

198

himself—or herself? Which, therefore, of his three parishes did the information refer to?

In which of them had a new curate been observed in the pub, talking to chapelgoers, to—heaven preserve us, it was too ridiculous—wearing daisy chains? How could he find out?

He checked himself again. The wretched letter was already doing its nasty work well. In spite of himself, he was giving it a lot of attention. He comforted himself with the thought that he had not been disturbed, or even intrigued, by its content—only by its existence and possible origin. He folded the letter neatly, put it back in its envelope and placed it inside his jacket again. There is, after all, no person more low on this earth than the sender of anonymous information, whatever its bearing, and the Vicar was surely right in his assumption that every decent person would agree with him on that point. He would destroy it as soon as it was possible in the fire to which, unconsciously, he was also committing its vulgar perpetrator.

Nevertheless, he felt contaminated by the fact that the horrid thing had been addressed to him, and still lay close to his person. A crank? Somebody with a twisted mind? Someone with an axe of his—or her—own to grind? There were in the missive no actual accusations made directly against anyone specific or named. It would have been easier to deal with if there had been. The bits about the curate were obviously cover for the real insinuation of sexual misdemeanour somewhere by a close member of his flock . . . he pulled himself up once more. He was speculating again about it, willy-nilly. For the first time ever, the real filthiness of any anonymous communication struck him with full force. However well balanced the recipient might be, once he had read the thing, its insidious work was done. Like Leontes, he had drunk—and seen the spider at the bottom of the cup.

Resolutely he pushed the matter from his mind; but when the fresh-faced boy who was now his curate presented himself at eleven o'clock to report, Costello found himself looking at him with new, doubting, eyes. Had he been wise to choose in such a hurry? Were the young man's credentials trustworthy, and as good as they appeared to be? Was his overflowing energy a healthy sign? Could it possibly be the outward manifestation of some eccentric—even warped—mind? Was there even the tiniest germ of truth in the preposterous story of the daisy chains? Surely he was not harbouring a pagan crank whose next move would be to perform black-magic rituals on a gravestone at midnight?

During their ensuing conversation, he was surprised at the number of times he rephrased a question, hoping to get some clue; but the frankness of the young man defeated him utterly. He really needed to give the curate warning that he did not take kindly to the idea of him drinking with the villagers—church or chapel; but how could he bring the subject up without disclosing the fact that someone had been talking, and that he had listened?

The innuendo about 'her' being 'in his house' at 5 am could not possibly refer to his curate, since at present the young man was in lodgings with a respectable couple. That, at any rate, was a relief; but it brought with it some feeling of foreboding, all the same. A handsome young man, so undeniably virile as Richard Ellis, must inevitably attract the attention of women, old as well as young, and thereby cause trouble of one kind or another. He could not help feeling that he had been most unwise to allow himself to be pitchforked into taking the first candidate who had offered himself. He had fouled up his long-cherished plan of getting assistance in his parishes by his own haste and faulty judgment. He should have waited until he found exactly the right man—one wholly dedicated to his calling, intelligent but not too sure of himself, preferably married but in any case not physically attractive. He had also always envisaged a man of a slightly lower social standing than himself, who would have looked up to him from all points of view. He sighed. He suspected Richard Ellis of intelligence, culture, birth too perhaps, equal to his own. Even in such rural unsophistication as his lot now lay, life could be full of problems.

Miss Taylor was the next recipient of a poison-pen letter.

Dear miss (it read)

It is lucky for some as i have not got no children going to school at the present time if i had i should have more to say to your face than them as can only say it all behind your back but i can tell you as they don't like it the children not doing there lessens proper but spend there time messing about with paint and going out for walks not always by herself neither

The row they make you can hear all over the village so everybody noes they can't be doing no proper work lerning to read and rite and such like as they ought but that is what your paid for and it wont be long before it is put in front of the proper quarters if things dont improve soon and i no who to rite to

But things ain't like they was once and teachers and there families dont keep theirselves respectable no more being friends with them as ain't no better than they should by why was she there at five oclock in the morning i should like to know there's more than one as see her and it arn't rite for a governesses sister to be showing her backside on the stage whoevver runs it specially making glad eyes at mr price from down the school if his master gets to here about his goings on you'll all be sacked and serve you rite good riddance to bad rubbish i say we ort to get a proper governess then as would keep the children in order so you have been warned.

from one as noes
what to do next

Miss Taylor's first reaction of utter disbelief turned to a gnawing anxiety before she reached the end. For a woman as consistently conscientious as she was about her duties as the village headteacher, there was always doubt as to whether the methods she was employing were suitable for the mix of children at any moment in her school. She had, of late, been trying out, if only tentatively, some new methods—free art was one of them. And it was true that she had tried to impress upon her infant teacher, Miss Keane (who was nearing retirement), the need for a little more freedom of movement and speech for the babies, and a little less fearful regimentation.

Ought she to be experimenting with new methods? Had they been proved? She had guessed that the village would talk, conservative as they were in most things, and even perhaps grumble a bit. She had hoped, if she were ever challenged, to be able to justify herself by gentle explanation and proof of the pudding in the children's work. This stab in the back was not expected, and made the self-searching guilt more persistent because she was denied the right to reply.

Then there was the attack on Miss Nellie. Again, Miss Taylor felt that there was just a germ of truth in the comments. Since the re-organization of The Magpies, and Nellie's inclusion in it, she had been different. 'Emancipated,' Nellie herself had said, and while Kathleen was truly glad to see her sister so obviously enjoying herself, she had to admit that the concert party had been a bit like the breach in the dike. She could only describe Nellie's behaviour on several occasions as 'flippant'; but Nellie had smiled her sweetest, humorously twisted smile at Kath's gentle remonstrance, and replied, 'So what? I'm doing nobody harm, am I? I really do think it's time all of us shook off the remnants of mourning for Prince Albert. Life *is* real, and I don't feel ready yet to agree that my heart is a muffled drum that's beating funeral marches to the grave! I'm happy and contented. Don't spoil it.'

But this idea about Monty Price: could that be the reason for the change in Miss Nellie? And who sent the dreadful letter, anyway? Miss Taylor sat back in her chair, and considered one awful possibility. Had Miss Keane, the infant teacher, become senile? Was this spiteful attack on her and her sister the crafty and subtle revenge of a woman who had bottled up feelings for so long that they had at last spilled over?

She threw the letter across to Nellie when she sat down, and heard the gasp of indignation as her sister's eye swept down to the bottom of it.

'How utterly appalling!' she exploded. 'Of all the——' words failed her.

'What are you going to do about it?' she asked. 'Who *can* it be?'

'Somebody with a knife into both of us, that's certain. I shall ignore it, absolutely. It is all we can do. I take it there's no truth in the Monty Price bit?'

Nellie's eyes flashed dangerously. 'What if there were? He's a bachelor, as far as I know, and I'm a spinster. But I'm certainly not "she" who was in "his" house at five o'clock in the morning. I imagine I should have had a good deal of difficulty getting in or out of his rooms at The Priory, especially as they happen to be right at the very top!' Her sense of humour was bubbling up as usual, but she restrained it, rather than upset Kath more.

'I'll put the thing where no one can find it, and then try to forget it,' Miss Taylor said. 'Though I'll keep my ears and eyes open. I may need the actual letter for proof, perhaps, one day. So I'd better hang on to it. Meanwhile, we must neither of us breathe it to a soul. Perhaps that's the worst thing of all about it. But I think, if no mention at all is made of it, the writer will be tempted to try again. I wonder if anyone else has received one?'

Someone else had. It was now Reg Pettigrew's turn.

Dear Reg

I am your frend and i don't like to see you being made a cuckoo on in your own house every time you go out hes there soon as your back his turned when your car as got out of the front yard mr marston i mean when is a washerwoman the happiest. when the clothes are up and the pegs in i hope you no what i mean and she ain't the only one. There's others besides her and him as play the same game and think folks don't see her when she goes off in his car before daylight.

yours respectfully

a friend.

Reg was standing by himself by the huge window of the kitchen, whose wide ledge served him as a sort of office. By the time he had finished reading it, there were red sparks glinting from his eyes, and his hair was standing up on his forehead like the hackles of a dog. His mouth was drawn back into a devilish grin that showed off his perfect teeth. Mixed with the Irish rage that the letter had touched off, there was more than a suggestion in his eyes and mouth that he was about to enjoy himself. He put the letter in his trousers pocket, picked up his cap and went outside. If Marston ran true to form, he would call at Stavesacre with a list of complaints and petty requests today as he did most Friday mornings, before going on to his office on the estate. Reg wondered if this new, weekly visit was part of a cover-up. If Marston called ostentatiously while Reg was at home, but before he went off to market, another visit later in the day would be more likely to pass unnoticed, even in a village.

Reg was leaning on the five-barred gate of the farmyard proper when Marston drove up. The agent got out of his car, and Reg obligingly opened the gate for him, shutting it again with deliberate care behind him. When both stood in the straw with backs to the gate, Reg took the letter from his pocket with an air of studied nonchalance, opened it out, and handed it to Marston, watching him with twinkling but red-flecked eyes as he read. Only those who knew Reg intimately could have told the difference between his normal twinkle and this glitter of fiendish, gleeful rage, inherited directly from Irish forebears. Certainly Marston could not. He flushed a dull red to the roots of his hair, and moved instinctively away; but when he looked up, Reg was still smiling, so he relaxed.

'Well?' said Reg. 'What about it? Are you going to strip and fight or shall I just thrash you?'

Whatever he was, Marston was no coward. He tossed off his tweed hat, and peeled off his jacket.

'Try!' was all he said. Like Reg, he had often envisaged this happening, sooner or later; and like Reg, he had come to the

204

conclusion that his skill would be more than a match for Reg's extra toughness. He had reckoned, however, without the temper he did not know the fury of, and the effect of the psychological fact that Reg was the injured, and he the potentially guilty party.

Reg's fist took him squarely between the eyes and sent him staggering back to the gate. The next moment, they were at it like two tigers. After a few minutes of well matched fisticuffs, Marston caught Reg fairly and squarely in the solar plexus, and knocked the wind out of him. He took the opportunity of Reg's momentary incapacity to run, across the freshly strawed yard towards the door of the barn, which stood open; but he had gone no more than a couple of steps when Reg recovered enough to divine his intention. Standing upright inside the door were a couple of pitchforks—the deadliest of all weapons ready to hand in any farmyard brawl. The man who gets to a pitchfork first has all the right on his side, and his opponent stands little chance of contradicting him thereafter. Reg sprang into action, and the fight became a race, in which the farmer's long, lithe legs were more than a match for the rather tubby, too well fed agent's. Reg sprang up the barn steps just ahead of Marston, who, seeing he was too late and now in grave danger, doubled back to the gate. Reg did not press his advantage over the fork. He leapt from the barn steps and gave chase again. The violent exercise and the few blows he had landed, to say nothing of the psychological fillip his faster speed had given him, had worked on his anger like a snuffer on a candle. He had lost all sense of vengeance now, and was fighting simply for the joy of it, of one man matched equally against another in a healthy trial of strength. Marston, seeing Reg had not taken advantage of getting a weapon, changed his mind about leaping the gate, and turned once more to face him. Reg lunged at his legs, threw him neatly, and then sat down on his chest, one leg each side of him on the straw, and pinioning his arms at biceps level with his own huge, powerful hands. Then he pulled the agent's body up from the squelchy straw, and raised it just enough to be able to push it down again with a thud into the manure that was beginning to ooze through its new covering. This manoeuvre seemed to delight him, and he was grinning now all over his face as Marston kept opening his mouth to yell, or swear, and then thinking better of it as his head went down again, even lower, into the muck. From his vantage point, Reg suddenly saw his opponent's expression change, and restrained himself for a moment, during which time Marston at last pulled a hand free. Reaching up, he tapped Reg lightly on the chest, and said, 'Mr Pettigrew, there's a lady wishing to speak to you,' as mildly as if they had merely been playing 'Brother, I'm bobbed' at a party.

Reg looked round, without getting up. Standing on the second rung of the gate, and leaning over the top bar, was Miss Nellie.

'Stop it! Now stop it! Do you hear me!' she was shouting, for all the world as if they were a couple of five-year-olds squabbling on the hearthrug. Reg shook his head, as if to clear it.

'Beg pardon?' he said, 'what did you say?' He continued to sit where he was, and both men looked foolishly towards the intruder, striving to make it appear as if it were the most natural thing in the world for two grown men to be rolling about in farmyard manure for a lark at nine o'clock on an autumn morning. Nellie climbed the gate, and came to the side of them.

'You should both be ashamed of yourselves,' she said severely. 'And I hope you are. Now get up, this minute.' Reg meekly got up, and gave Marston his hand to help him regain his feet. 'Now shake hands,' the lady commanded. Reg obediently held out his paw, and suddenly the funny side of it all caught him on his funny bone. He began to laugh. He laughed and laughed, great peals that caused him to catch his breath and choke. His eyes watered and he pulled his handkerchief out to dry them, stuffing it against his mouth to try to stop the next paroxysm. When his eyes were dry enough, he took a look at Miss Nellie. She, too, was now helpless with laughter, though indeed it was only of the catching variety. She had seen nothing funny whatsoever in the situation, but in her relief at Reg's reaction she let herself be infected. She didn't know what she was laughing at, but she was enjoying the sight of Reg's helplessness. Watching them both, Marston himself joined in after a moment, giving voice to such feeble little sniggers at first that it sent the other two off again into fresh fits of mirth.

It burnt itself out at last, and they all stood looking foolish and sheepish at each other. Nellie recovered herself first, and mumbling hasty farewells she scrambled back to the gate. Both men leapt forward to open it for her, and she went through and sped down the road like a scared chicken.

The antagonists eyed each other.

'Is there any truth in it?' Reg asked mildly. Marston shook his head. 'Not in the way that bloody letter reads, no,' he replied. 'I get on well with your wife. You know we dance well together as partners in old-time dancing. I have called three or four times for a cup of coffee. But if you don't trust me, you might at least trust Gwen not to be a fool.'

Reg thought bitterly that Marston obviously did not know the truth about the gradually cooling atmosphere at Stavesacre—which meant in turn, of course, that he probably was as innocent of real provocation as he was claiming to be.

'Who do you reckon wrote the bloody thing?' he asked, taking it again from his pocket.

They studied it together, leaning side by side over the gate. Marston's back and Reg's knees were wet with the stinking farmyard muck.

'We'd better keep quiet about it,' said Marston. 'If we keep our heads down and our ears open, we shall be a lot more likely to find out. Whoever it is, it will have to be stopped; but for all our sakes—specially Gwen's—we can't let on about it now.' Reg nodded. 'That's about how I see it,' he said. 'I hope

Miss Nellie don't split on us, about this morning. But she won't. She's a real good sort, Nellie is. There's more life in her little finger than most women have all over 'em.'

Marston nodded. 'I'll slip off and have a bath. I shall tell Jean I slipped over in your yard.' There was a look of appeal in his statement. Reg nodded, and watched him climb into his car. They held up their hands to each other in mutual salute as the car drew away. Reg went back to work thinking it was a long time since he had enjoyed himself so much, though he reflected soberly on the situation and on any possible re-appearance of the anonymous troublemaker. Try as he would, he could find no possible candidate for the authorship. He succeeded fairly well in pushing the whole incident from his mind, though when he turned over in bed for many a night afterwards, he found the lines of writing clear before his closed eyes again, and somewhere deep inside him a voice whispered that there was no smoke without fire.

When Nurse Hardy opened the letter addressed to her, she got into her car and drove straight to Cudweed. She was a bit thrown at finding Elsie Winters washing up at the kitchen sink, while Jack was drinking a cup of tea in his chair by the gate.

Elsie welcomed Nurse in and offered her a cup of tea, which she declined, saying she had a large round to cover that day, but wanted Jack's advice about one of the Roslins. He took the hint, and said he'd go and get her the beastings he'd promised her for a custard when he next had a cow calve, if she could wait a minute.

'I'll wait in the car, then,' she said. 'I shan't keep you a minute about the Roslins.'

When he handed the jar of beastings through the car win-dow, she said, 'Jack, I must talk to you in private. Where can we meet without being seen?'

He seemed to understand immediately. 'You'd better come back tonight after dark,' he said. 'That would be safer than me coming to see you. Leave your car against the gate to

Stavesacre wood, and I'll come round and pick you up. Eight o'clock?'

She nodded briskly. He stood away from the car, and she turned it, waving to Elsie as she did so, and calling, 'Thanks a lot for the advice,' in a hearty tone for Elsie's benefit.

The day seemed very long to them both, but a few minutes after eight Nurse was sitting opposite to Jack across the grate at Cudweed. The door was locked, and the curtains carefully drawn, though neither could have told why. They felt a sort of protective instinct, sharpened by events.

'Now, what's the trouble?' Jack said, coming in his direct way straight to the point. 'It's an anonymous letter, isn't it?' She gaped at him. 'How did you know?'

'Because I had one of the damn things myself, a day or two back. I hoped you'd never find out, but as soon as I saw you this morning, I guessed. Where is it? Can I see it?'

She passed it over.

Dear Nurse (it said)
You think becuase we keep ourself to ourself in these parts we don't no how folks as come from london carry on but we do for all your london airs and graices you can't come it over me and you may make out to be a miss but i no as your really a missus and not a widow neither why don't you draw no widows pension if you are perhaps thats why you miss it so much and him being a widow-man no doubt hes as glad of it as you are but I want to let you no as you ain't the only one as gets all she wants up at Cudweed though not in the middle of the night theres plenty of time in daylight and he don't care when or where did you do it on the mat in front of the fire its no good you trying to deny it because I see you with my own eyes getting dressed again with only your chemise and britches on bold as brass at five o'clock in the morning you don't no whose watching you do you i'll bet you never thought any body would find out about that but it will have to stop or it will be a sorry day for him i shall tell everybody what i see with

my own eyes if you don't stop going to see him and meeting
him whenever you get the chance so i give you two weeks to
make up your mind then i shall make the matter plain to them
as it concerns there's some of us as would be glad to see the
back of such as you. you london whore.

from somebody what noes a lot.

She sat staring into the fire while he read it, looking, as she
always did, clean and compact, though at the moment wearing a strange, sad dignity instead of her usual merry, comfortable air. He clenched his hands as he looked at her, and swore
long and low under his breath at the content of the letter.

'Can I see yours?' she said. 'What did it say?'

'Much the same,' he answered, 'only in a lot filthier language. I burnt it. I was afraid if I even so much as mentioned it,
you'd get to hear somehow. I just hoped you never would. I
never even thought about whoever it is actually writing such
filth to you, until you drove up this morning. I'm sorry. It's all
my fault. I've lived in a village long enough to know you can't
hide anything. I ought to have known somebody would find
out if I brought you home here in the middle of the night.'

'Don't be silly,' she said. 'If I had to lose my reputation
every time I'm seen alone with a man at night I shouldn't have
a shred left by now. It happens two or three times a week. I'm
not concerned about myself—it's the stink around you that
worries me. This is your own ground, and you've got to stop.
I can always look for another job somewhere else. Time I did,
perhaps, when this sort of thing happens.'

He sat down again in his own chair, at loss for words. He
could not bear the thought of her going out of his life, and felt
bereft already.

'What can we do? Is there any way we can stop the gossip?'
she asked.

'I wish I knew who it was,' he growled. 'I'd take a horse-
whip to him!'

'Her,' she corrected. 'I'd stake my life it's a woman.'

He shook his head. 'Can't be,' he said. 'It's somebody who hasn't got enough to do—most women have too much—and it's somebody who thinks and talks smutty by nature. I really can't believe any woman could write the sort of stuff there was in the one I had. Somebody like that Roslin man, for instance. You don't think he's been hanging about round here all this time, do you? After all, we don't know where he went that night—he knew I was with you up at the cottage. He was quite likely down here seeing what he could pinch from the yard. He could have been watching through a gap in the curtains, like as not.'

It did, indeed, seem a likely possibility.

'Well, he'll have more to add to his lies, if he's looking in now,' she said. 'I must go before The Scandalmonger Strikes Again! Cheer up, Jack. I'm sorry now that I let it upset me, or that I worried you with it. Let 'em talk. There's no truth in it, and we can ride the storm, if it ever breaks, with clear consciences.' She rose, ruffling her curls.

'No, don't go!' he said impulsively. 'There is another way we could scotch the gossip. We could make it true—and legal. That would be one in the eye for whoever it is. Would you even consider it?'

He was as calm now, and under full self-control, as if asking middle-aged ladies to marry him was as much in his line as milking his cows. She stood staring at him as if she had been slugged on the head, and robbed of all reason. Her face lit up for one joyous moment before she collapsed again into the chair, and started to cry.

'Don't cry,' he said. 'You don't have to worry. I knew you wouldn't, but I've been wanting to ask you ever since that night—' he nodded towards the letter.

'But I would!' she said. 'I would! That's what makes it so awful. I've known you wanted to ask me—women always know. But I hoped you wouldn't. It isn't that I don't want to marry you. I can't—I'm still married! That's what that letter meant. Somebody has found out he's still alive.'

211

'Tell me about it, will you?' he said, putting the kettle over the fire in a very matter-of-fact way.

'Nothing to tell, really. A war-time marriage between a silly young nurse and a medical student. He went to the war, and came back different. He was cruel in every way it is possible for a man to be cruel to a woman, deliberately, painstakingly cruel. When I couldn't stand it any longer I disappeared for a while, then pretended I was a widow and got this job. There was such as call for nurses willing to do district work that nobody asked too many questions. I don't suppose it would have made any difference if I had told the truth, but I just wanted to put it all behind me and start again. And I've managed it for twenty odd years! But as you say, you can't keep a secret in a village.'

'When did you last hear of him?'

'Oh, about ten years ago—but what difference does that make?'

'You must get a divorce,' he said, stoutly.

She shook her head. 'Don't daydream, Jack,' she said. 'We have to face the facts. I'm the guilty party, for one thing. I left him. I can't prove anything against him after all these years. But in any case, you couldn't marry a divorced woman.'

'Oh, couldn't I? Let's have a cup of tea, shall we?'

He took the kettle from the hob, and deftly made and poured the tea. She watched him. When she took the cup from him, he laid his hand on her curls, and ruffled them. The tears slipped down her face. 'We could have been so happy,' she said.

'We shall be so happy,' he answered. 'Here's to Mr and Mrs Jack Marriatt of Cudweed, at some time in the future, however long it takes.'

She took hope and courage from him. 'Fancy!' she said. 'I'll bet whoever wrote that letter never intended it to have such a drastic result!'

'Leave everything to me for the time being,' he said. 'And don't destroy your letter. We may need a bit of evidence if we ever set eyes on that Roslin again. Mum's the word about everything, for a little while. We shall have to act just as we always have done towards each other—but you know now how I feel about you, and I shan't give up easily.'

'Nor me,' she said. She put out her hand, and he took it in both his. It was enough.

The last letter went to Gwen Pettigrew.

Dear madam

If you want to know where your husband goes to get a bit extra to what you give him i can tell you. he didn't take that diddiki woman into the cottage up there for nothing o no he didn't if you have missed anything from your pantry you no where its gone and wood and all he used to supply her with as well as presents for the kids where did he go on xmas eve last year you didnt no did you but i did i see him go up there on the tractor and come back round the other way so as he could call at the pub on his way home and then you wouldn't no—you just think how many times he used to go out in the dark when she were up there thats where he went I no and that nurse were in the no as well because she is as bad as he is birds of a feather flock together she'll keep his secret as long as he keeps hers because if she's seen him with his trousers down round the diddiki bitch i reckon he knows about what she's up to i shall keep watch to see if he ever calls at number 3 council houses and if he does i shall rite again to let you know and if you want any more news then perhaps you will be willing to pay for it to keep it quiet or to let the cat out of the bag witchever you like so save your money up and keep yourself to yourself i shouldn't care to have anything to do with him myself after him being with her you don't no what she's got he could be bringing home one of these days so till then i shall say no more

from An other

Gwen read it several times over, then folded it neatly and placed it carefully in the secret drawer of her bureau, to which only she had the key.

Everything comes to those who wait. She was in no hurry.

15 All's fair in love and war

The gentle tide of everyday life moved backwards and forwards over the village as it had done for centuries, silently
jostling and rounding off the pebbles in its path. Now and then
it threw pieces of flotsam to the surface for inspection, or left
remnants of old scandals like jetsam on the beach. It removed
dear old Grandad Woodward from the scene at Pellmell,
protesting to the last that all he'd got the matter with him was a
cold on his chest and he'd never had to stop abed with such a
thing in all his life before and wasn't going to now.

'Rest,' shouted Dr Leathers. 'You need a LONG REST to put
you right.'

'I've wore one all my life,' wheezed the old man, 'on'y we
allus called 'em undershirts.' Nothing and nobody could keep
him in bed, and he simply collapsed one morning on the
kitchen floor at Timmy's feet. He was much missed in every
way, and his contemporaries took his death as a personal
affront. Old Sammy regaled Reg with tales of sudden death in
his family that reached right back to one of his great uncles
who had died of excitement at seeing old Queen Vicky on the
only time she ever visited The Priory, and another cousin who
had hung herself with a stocking from the bottom of her own
bed. 'Masterpiece how she managed it,' said Sam, 'but the

coroner brought it in fellindisee, or whatever they call it. We couldn't make it out at all, an' to this day there's them as think he done it. But the Tibbses were allus ones for 'anging their-selves, an' she were a Tibbs by birth, d'yer see. So it's quite likely as she done it herself, arter all.'

Aunt Mabel argued for two whole days that Grandad at Pellmell wasn't as old as he'd made out to be, because when they were at school together he was the same age as she was, and she wouldn't turn eighty-two till Michaelmas. Grandad had been eighty-five, and Aunt Mabel was, in fact, in her eighty-fourth year. May unwisely attempted to prove this to her, and was rewarded with one of Aunt Mabel's awful fits of sulking, when for four or five days together she would gloom in total silence. Her face, normally rosy and animated, settled into heavy folds of skin around the jowls and dewlap, while the corners of her mouth turned down to lose themselves among the sagging folds of skin. When she spoke at all, her voice was a reproach to all other living creatures, as if it was their fault and because of their personal vindictiveness that she was so old and unhappy. Her lower lip hung loose and flabby—like a pig's behind, Uncle Bert said to May. He would have used a coarser expression for that particular part of porcine anatomy if he hadn't happened to be depressed as well, mostly on account of Aunt Mabel's sulks.

Now and again, the world outside reached out and touched them. Aeroplanes, once so rare, now crossed their skies so frequently that no one even bothered to look up. There was a fleeting sense of personal involvement with the goings on of governments when one of Charlie's young nephews got killed in an air crash soon after joining the RAF. Several people laid his death directly at the door of a German called Hitler who had begun to be talked about in the The Star and Don's shop, and whose name intruded on more and more supper tables as even the poorest and most conservative homes yielded to the lure of the wireless set.

Only George Willis stood firm against it. 'I don't want one

215

o' the bloody things,' he said to Reg. 'It would be blarin' out when I wanted to go to bed. 'Enery 'All ain't much in my line.'

'You can turn 'em off, you know,' Reg replied.

'Can yer? Well, I still don't see no sense in spending good money to keep a bloody wireless going as is turned off. Anyways, I don't want one o' the bloody things.'

Rumour began to spread that Charlie's brother Don, the cobbler, was making sheep's eyes at Poor Alice, who certainly appeared to be blossoming out a bit, and seemed to have a fair number of shoes to be mended all at once. Mrs Watson reported to Pellmell that she thought there must be something in it, because she had passed Don's door when Alice was standing in it, and they were deep in conversation, though not about boots or shoes.

'Did you hear what they said then, really?'

'Dearie me O, yes. Just as I went by, she said to him, "We have got a lot o' mice in our pantry".'

'Aye! Well that's enough to raise any man's temperature,' said Timmy.

There came a morning when not a single Roslin child turned up at school. By lunch time the neighbours had noticed how quiet everything was at No. 3, and finally Mrs Bluett persuaded her youngest brother, who lived with her as a lodger, to go and investigate.

'I said to our Hughie, I says, Do go an' knock on the door, or look through the winder,' she shrieked at May, though with her head turned so that Aunt Mabel could lip-read from the overworked mouth that she couldn't hear. 'For all we know, I says, they may all be a-layin' there in their own blood wi' their throats cut. After all, I says, they ain't the same nature as we are, bein' diddikis. What's bred in the bone'll come out in the flesh, I says, and you often 'ear o' gyppoes and diddikis an' the like murdering and suiciding each other! So he went as soon as he'd finished his dinner, an' comes back again. "There ain't neither 'ide nor 'air of 'em," 'e says, "dead or alive". An' that's the truth, if I die where I stand wi' this counter in my 'and. They're gone, vamoosled, abscondled clean as a whistle, right down to that second set o' twins. Hughie went down to the school, and told the governess, and she got the policeman to come, an' he broke in—well, come to that, the door weren't locked, else our Hughie wouldn't a bin able to force his entrance, like, in the first place. All the bits and sticks o' furniture as Nurse got for 'em is still there. PC Abbott said he thought perhaps as that Roslin 'ad come in the night wi' a car, an' took 'em all away, 'cos the police have seen him 'anging about round 'ere lately. Hughie said as a car wouldn't be no good for all that tribe. He said Roslin would have had to have had a pantechknicker at least, or a charrabank, to get 'em all in, an' if so, how was it we didn't none of us hear it? But gone they have, and not before time, though I must say the woman herself were a nice enough gal. But I never neighboured with her, only to pass the time o' day an' such like.' She paused at last with her mouth squarely open, and attempted such a smile as she prepared to quit the stage, that as Aunt Mabel said afterwards 'it very near showed 'em what she'd had for dinner'.

Sonny was quick off the mark to secure the empty house, and as there was no serious opposition to his application, he was soon moved in. The atmosphere in Martha's cottage was not much improved by the re-arrangement, however. Maudie and Mog were not on very good terms with each other, and Mog had often used the excuse of the overcrowding at home as a reason for stopping in town, close to his work, at night. After Sonny's departure, he had to invent other excuses. Maudie, with the help of her brothers, saw through them all. Mog had been seen far too often with Margie in his car for his tales to sound well in his wife's ears. She tackled him about it, but he flew into a temper and swore he'd only given Margie a lift home when she'd been playing in a pub and he'd happened to go in there for a drink.

'I'll drink her if I ever catch her in your car again,' Maudie screamed, 'so you just watch out, Mog Evans!'

Whippet deplored a situation that was liable to cause talk

and scandal, because after all he was now a churchwarden, and as he said you couldn't come near pitch without being defiled; but he had less sympathy with Maudie than he might have had. She was a little spitfire, and as lazy as they come. His private opinion was that 'a slap or two o' the skull' from Mog would do her the world of good.

Jack Marriatt had been observed, dressed up, going to town several times 'on business'. Mog and Margie had both seen him going into 'the lawyer's place'.

'Making his will, I daresay,' said George Willis. 'I can't think what else he can want with a bloody lawyer. I hope as poor old Jack's all right, not bad with a cancer or somethink. It don't seem healthy for a strong chap like him to be makin' a will unless he's got a good idea as 'is next new suit'll be made o' wood. Got nobody close to leave it all to, anyway, now his missus has gone.'

'I dare say Elsie Winters'll come in for a nice bit,' was Sally Watts's opinion. She was a friend of Elsie's, at least, as good a friend as Elsie allowed anybody to be. Sally was aware of the care Elsie took of the widowed farmer, and envied her friend that interesting work as well as the windfall that might one day come her way.

In fact, Jack Marriatt's visits to his solicitor had surpassed even his wildest hopes. Nurse's husband had easily been located. He was now a doctor of some standing attached to a London hospital, and had been living for many years with a charming ex-sister who was his wife in every respect except law. She had taken his name, and no one in their circle knew of their true relationship. He had been just as frustrated and resentful at Nurse's continued existence—as far as he knew—as she of his. He had readily agreed to be divorced, and presented Jack's solicitor with the usual cooked-up evidence against himself. Nurse's petition had gone in from the London address of her married sister where 'for safety's sake' she had maintained a room, and for once the village bloodhounds had failed to follow the scent. She would be free some time before

218

Easter. In spite of their circumspection, however, the news of the friendship between Jack and Nurse had begun to trickle round and they were the butt of many coarse jokes in all three villages. Mrs Jeffs, sniffing a possible romance, had tried to pump Miss Nellie and Elsie as they cleaned the church brasses, using as a sprat to catch the mackerel she wanted an account of how both her husbands had proposed to her. The first had been a very romantic affair—in a cellar to which the guests had been forced to retire during a revolt by the Pueblo Indians in Mexico City; but the second—Tom Jeffs—had happened on top of a London omnibus.

'Of course,' she said, 'I had known Tom long ago, before I ever left England. He was not of my own class, but I had always liked him, and I was very lonely after my first dear husband died, in spite of having Royal and the two girls. But I took the chance when Tom asked me to marry him, and it was done before I knew what I was letting myself in for. He told me he had two children, both grown up. They came to the wedding. It was only afterwards he brought the others home—one at a time. Then he died, and left me with all of them to look after. Of course, I was tied hand and foot, then, so that when another old friend of mine took a job on the Malay Straits Times and asked me to marry him and go with him, in fairness to the children I had to refuse. But I was sorry, because I knew Singapore quite well, and I should have quite enjoyed going back there. Well, well, so there really is more than casual friendship between Nurse and Jack Marriatt, is there?'

She looked from one to the other. Elsie was polishing with her usual zest, and pursed her lips even tighter than usual to prevent a wisp of scandal escaping them. Miss Nellie said she'd only heard what everybody was saying, but for her part she could think of nothing nicer than if it did happen to be true. Everybody needed something to think about at this time of year, she said, with the weather so awful and the news so worrying. Her sister and the Professor had begun really to

219

worry in case there might be another war soon. And Rev. Ellis had said he could not see how it could be avoided, if Britain was to keep her honour.

He had, indeed, said so to the Professor—and both had sat silent, each knowing the other was mentally quoting Falstaff on the subject of honour. The Professor looked with pity on the picture of health and strength before him, and understood that, dog-collar or no dog-collar, men like Richard must be those such a catastrophe would first sacrifice. Richard looked back at the noble old face under its bald, peaked dome, and speculated with horror that the next war would be no respecter of civilians, age or sex.

So while war and romance hung in the air above and about them, and spring still held back, Maudie declared war on her own behalf. The postman had brought her a letter.

Dear Maudie

if you want to see what your husband is up to with margie you can catch him saying goodnight to her in the lane between the church and the star when he brings her home after being together saturday nights when the pubs are closed so now i'll say no more but you take my advice and see for yourself come next saturday night

from one as wishes you well.

Maudie showed it to her mother; to Whippet; to Sonny and his wife, and then to Mrs Bluett, Mrs Woods, and everybody else who would read it, and join their indignation about her husband's goings-on to her own. Margie was away, stopping in town, but her mother got to hear about it, and went down and slapped Maudie's face.

The village might as well have been going up in flames. From end to end and from side to side the bush fire raged, even from top to bottom of The System. Somehow or other they were all involved in it, or at least chose to be.

Jack Marriatt and Nurse were made uneasy. When the Roslins had disappeared, they had felt sure Roslin had been the

220

culprit with regard to the letters they had received; but he had gone now—though that did not prevent him from writing letters, of course. Maudie's had, however, been posted in the village letter-box. Several people quizzed May as to who had been seen posting letters, and in spite of herself, she began to take notice. As for Aunt Mabel, she barely took her eyes off the path in case she missed the vital clue.

Jack tried to bolster Nurse, asking hypothetically what harm anybody could do them now.

'I don't know,' she replied. 'It just spoils things a bit. There's another three weeks to go before the decree becomes absolute. Remember Mrs Simpson? There is such a thing as the King's Proctor, and after all there *was* some collusion. We had better not be seen together from now till Easter.'

Miss Taylor and Nellie discussed Maudie's letter in the light of the one carefully folded and locked away in her bureau. Miss Taylor voiced her suspicion about Miss Keane for the first time aloud.

'I keep watching her,' she said, 'but she seems normal enough, if a bit more waspish than usual. She really was very nasty about Jack Marriatt's friendship with Nurse. I suppose it could be that a frustrated old maid might want to make trouble for anybody young and pretty, like Maudie, who had a husband as handsome and lively as Mog Evans.'

Miss Nellie considered the possibility with more than a suspicion of a twinkle.

'What a lovely plot for a novel,' she said, 'with so many obvious suspects scattered about. There's you, and me, and Charity and Selena and poor Alice and Gladys—and several more as well as Miss Keane. I think I shall have to become Nellie the Sleuth, to stop the finger of suspicion pointing at me.'

Reg and Marston discussed it amicably in the quiet of the woods. It was Reg who put forward the suggestion that in all probability other people had had letters too, but had had enough sense to keep quiet. They both felt that perhaps the time had come to go to the police—but the personal nature of the attack on Gwen and the agent dissuaded them.

'It's no good washing dirty linen in public, even if it wasn't you that made it mucky in the first place,' Marston said.

Reg nodded. 'And it's no use stirring up stinking mud. It only makes it stink worse.' They were getting on better together than ever before.

The Vicar was if anything relieved to hear of Maudie's letter. He could now feel with some degree of certainty that the writer was a crank, and that there was nothing very dire to discover about Richard Ellis, who was after all proving a great help and becoming very popular, even though his liberal ideas and uninhibited behaviour still caused talk in the village and displeasure in the vicarage.

The nine days' wonder of the letter had just about run its course by the weekend. It was getting on for closing time on the Saturday evening when Maudie pushed open the door of The Star and went into the bar. Dolly was serving there, as Maudie ordered a bottle of ginger beer and a packet of crisps. She drank the mineral water as slowly as possible, with her eye on the clock. Then she produced a string bag from her large leather shopping-bag, and asked Dolly for two dozen more bottles of ginger beer. The order surprised Dolly. 'Going to have a party?' she asked. Maudie smiled, pert but sour. 'Sort of,' she said. Dolly regretted that she couldn't supply so many. 'Doesn't matter what it is, as long as they are little bottles,' Maudie said, and accepted the mixture Dolly produced. Maudie tucked the bottles into her two bags, and said goodnight, leaving well before the men would turn out.

An hour later, Mog Evans's car pulled into the narrow lane between the churchyard walls and the pub. He switched the lights down to the feeble sidelights and offered his passenger a cigarette. As the match glowed, it lit up the interior of the car and with it the unmistakable red halo of Margie's curls. Mog pulled down the window to throw the match out, and voices wafted on to the air.

'Goo'night, then. Thanks for the lift.'

'Any time, if I'm coming this way.'

'Ooh, I'm tired!'

'Give us a kiss then. There's no harm in a kiss, is there?'

Two cigarette ends glowed, very much closer together than before. Then they were stubbed out.

Crash! Bonk! Crash! The windscreen shattered into radiating cracks.

'Nefoedd! Jesu mawr! Duw! Duw! What the bloody hell? Keep your head down, Margie.' Margie was screaming with fright, cowering in the seat. Smash! Rattle! Crash! (Another window gone.) Mog pushed the door open, and got out. A full bottle of soda water took him in the abdomen, and burst at his feet. A half-moon came out from behind the clouds.

'It's her!' screamed Margie. 'It's her! In the churchyard!' She attempted to scramble from the car. Three bottles of pop in quick succession came from behind the churchyard wall. One hit the car at roof level and smashed, pouring cold, sticky, red pop down the cleft of Margie's bosom. Another caught her knee, and she howled with pain. Mog was undecided about making a rush for it, or seeking what shelter there was in the car. Maudie had all the advantages. She was a good four feet higher than they were, and protected by a six-hundred-year-old wall, except for the instant it took her to pop up and discharge her dangerous missiles. She continued to pelt the car and its occupants. Margie, who now had a few superficial cuts as the result of a particularly well aimed bottle which finished off the windscreen, began to scream in earnest, high, ear-splitting screams of genuine terror. Mog emerged again, roaring Welsh oaths, discretion cast to the wind. Maudie joined in. 'I said I'd give her drink enough,' she bawled. 'Red-headed whore! I'll kiss her for you where she won't like it! Take that, you whoring bitch! I'll kiss you, that I will!' The last, to her husband, was accompanied by a full bottle of ginger beer aimed accurately at his mouth. It split his lip, and filled him with uncontrollable fury at the sudden pain. 'Gasp-y-cythreal!'

The doors of The Star had been opened gingerly, and Charlie and Dolly could be seen peeping through, one head above the other. Candles began to flicker in windows all down the street, and casements to be cautiously opened.

Mog yelled instructions to Margie. 'Keep down inside the car until you think it's safe, and then make a bolt for it,' he said. He pulled his jacket up over his ears, and ran, while Maudie expended the last of her missiles on him. She then hung over the wall, still yelling insults to the sobbing redhead.

Mog pulled Maudie down in one hand, and with his other dealt her exactly the medicine Whippet had prescribed for her. She fought like a wildcat, and they continued to do battle among the graves until at last he overpowered her, pinioned her arms, and led her out into the road. Meanwhile, Margie had scrambled out of the car and was searching underneath it among the debris of glass and bottles for the high-heeled shoe she had lost in her previous bid to escape. She found it at last, and slipped it on. Her heavy make-up had been ruined by tears, and her dress was streaked with sticky red stripes. Her short, cheap fur coat was likewise plastered, and smeared with the blood that trickled from several cuts. A poor, soggy, bedraggled Margie it was that finally began to cockle down the lane towards home on her five-inch heels, and one who had paid dearly for a lift and a bit of canoodling. The truth was that all Margie's vices lay in her appearance and her vitality, and her refusal to hide the talent that she possessed for playing jazz on the piano. She had never in her twenty-two years so far 'gone too far' with a man, especially one already married, though she had been sorely tempted many times. She had been very strictly brought up, and so far, training had held firm.

As it happened, she ran straight into the arms of her father. He had been roused by the commotion and hung his head out of the bedroom window. From afar he had recognized the screams, and had said to his wife, 'That's our Margie.' He slipped his trousers on over the shirt he was still wearing in bed, and once downstairs, put on his boots. Then he took up the thin piece of dowel his wife used as a copper stick, and waited inside the door. When Margie came through it, he caught her and carried her into the kitchen. Then he laid her across his knee, turned up her clothes as if she had been a child, and 'tanned her backside good and proper'.

'Don't, Will! That's enough! Don't, Will,' her mother pleaded, and at last he threw the copper stick away.

'That'll teach you a lesson,' he said, as Margie pulled herself away from him. 'No gal o' mine gets herself mixed up with another woman's 'usband. If you stop in my house, you'll never go near a pub again and you'll be in bed, same as the others, at ten o'clock. An' if that don't suit yer, yer can get out, and stop there!'

She had more bruises next morning than those caused by Maudie's missiles. On Monday morning she went to work as usual, but it was many, many months before the village saw her again. She might just as well be hung for a sheep as a lamb.

16 No cross, no crown

Chance had thrown Eddie Linsell and Richard Ellis together more than once, and they had left each other again with mutual respect and liking. Richard never ceased to be surprised at the sincerity and depth of belief that kept the chapel going against many material odds. He often envied the simplicity of the faith in which its members trusted, while at the same time sometimes regretting, even deploring, the puritanic bigotry that often accompanied it. Old Harriet Payne, for instance, on whom Richard often called. Chapel she was, and chapel she had been since the day of her birth, and her father and mother before her. Nevertheless, 'the parson' was given great respect, and she expected to be visited by him in her turn.

Richard had been given the tip by Miss Taylor that he was expected to visit Harriet and had found himself welcome, regaled with tea and her special 'balm cake'. She was making a rag doll (a betsy, she called it) for the new baby up at Dindle. Every new baby got one of Harriet's betsies, complete with clothes. All the other clothes were made to be taken off and on, but the knickers were sewn securely to the doll, both at top and bottom, to prevent any undue curiosity about the doll's sex. It was at Harriet's that the curate had first encountered Eddie, who had called on Harriet on his way home from work, and was still wearing his working clothes. Richard had soon made the younger man feel at ease, and over tea and cake they began to touch on the dangerous matter of religious denomination. He could see at once that both Harriet and Eddie were taking up defensive, even defiant, positions.

'In my father's house are many mansions,' he said, 'Shall we agree that there are also many doors?' The look Eddie gave him felt like a benison, and old Harriet had smiled to show she understood. In fact, it was she who broke the rather awkward silence with a chuckle.

'When I were at home, before I married my Harry,' she said, 'I lived with my fam'ly in a tiny little cottage as weren't no where near big enough for us all. I were a strapping great gal, in them days, an' my mother were a very big woman; but all our doors were little—you had to stoop to get underneath the lintel and turn sideways to get through 'em. We were getting tea ready one Sunday I remember when the preacher were coming (and my Harry). We were fetching things out o' the pantry an' setting them on the table. We kep' getting in each other's way, an' at last my mother lost her patience with me. "Dear O Law, Hatty," she says. "If you an' me ever meet in heaven, I'll be bound it'll be in a doorway!" '

Richard marvelled at the ease with which she had broken both social and ecumenical tension with her reminiscence. He longed for more, and in time got them. Now he called on her not out of duty, but because he loved to hear her talk about the village in days gone by. He also enjoyed her particular brand of philosophy.

One day, he found her most distressed at the loss of a ten-shilling note she had received from May at the post office for her old-age pension.

'I know I had it,' she said, 'and I remember putting it down on the chest o' drawers. But when I went to get it to pay for my milk, it had gone. I declare I've looked high and low, but nowhere can I find it.' Richard took the hint, but searched in vain.

'If I can't find it,' she said, 'I shall know what to do. I shall do as the 'ymn says, an' take it to the Lord in prayer.'

Richard was tongue-tied. He knew she expected an answer, but somehow he could not bring himself to condone a resort to prayer where the matter was so inconsequential, and any practical answer so much to be doubted. He remained silent, and she took him up. 'Ah, young man, I dessay you think as your God wouldn't want to be bothered with listening to a poor old woman what had lost her old-age pension. But mine would—doesn't the bible tell us that he knows if a sparrow falls to the ground?'

Richard was ashamed. 'Of course you must pray about it, if it will help you,' he said, gently.

She inclined her head regally, before replying. 'I shall,' she said, 'an' you'll see. But I shan't worry 'Im Above about it till I've done all I can to help myself.'

He called again the next week, and found her very elated. She showed him a crumpled, dirty ten-shilling note, and he asked, twinkling, 'Did you have to pray?'

She nodded brightly, her old eyes matching his own. 'That very night, afore I went to bed. I swep' and dusted this room till I could ha' found a bee's knee if there'd been one there. But there wasn't no sign at all o' my money. So I went to bed, and got my nightie on, an' said my prayers, but I didn't want to worry 'Im, yet. Then just as I were standing aside my bed, after getting up from my knees, you understand, the loss come over me all over again, till I could ha' cried. An' I put my hands together, and shut my eyes, and I looked up and said, "O Lord, do 'elp me to find my pension! You know as I can't afford to lose it, an' it wasn't my fault. I could swear on my bible oath as I put it on my chest o' drawers." An' He spoke to me, right in my ear. I 'eard His Voice, as clear as if it might be you a-speaking to me now. An' He says, "You silly old fool, Harriet Payne! You've got *two* chests o' drawers, ain't you?" An' I opened my eyes, and turned round 'cos I were leaning against the chest o' drawers next to my bed, an' there it laid, my ten-shilling note, right on the top—under my hair-tidy, where I'd left it.'

Richard was on his way visiting, riding his old bike, when just before he reached the bounds of the village proper, he caught sight of Eddie Linsell apparently on his way home from work, though it was still only mid-afternoon. Eddie, too, was on his old bike, but he was travelling very slowly, and wobbling from side to side of the road. Richard had recognized his back, and had been striving to catch up with him, but he braked a bit on observing Eddie's erratic progress, and fell behind again. What was the matter with Eddie? He surely couldn't be drunk? The curate had been told that drink was one of the demons Eddie wrestled with from the pulpit on many occasions, and that he was a tee-totaller.

Eddie did not look round, and Richard continued behind him, wishing sincerely that it had been any other than he that had witnessed the young man's downfall, if such it was. Then Eddie suddenly stopped pedalling, and it seemed as if the cycle balanced of its own accord for a long moment. Then bike and rider crashed to the ground.

The young clergyman was on his knees beside the thin figure of Eddie almost as soon as he fell, and his first instinct was to stay there long enough to breathe a prayer of contrition for unworthy suspicion. Eddie was not drunk, but ill. His face was the colour of old putty, and he was having difficulty with his breathing. At present, he was in a deep swoon, but he came round after a minute or two, and began to cough—long spells that left him breathless and almost without the strength to draw enough breath to cough again. When at last it was possible, Richard got him on his feet, and leaving both cycles where they were they set off to cover the long half-mile to Eddie's home. Richard saw him to bed in his tiny, spotless bedroom, and went downstairs. He spoke to Mrs Linsell, Eddie's mother.

'I'm afraid Eddie is very ill, Mrs Linsell,' he said. 'I think you had better let me go straight for the doctor.'

She looked worried, but firm. 'Oh, no, sir, don't do that. Our Eddie'll be all right. He's been chesty every since he was a littl'un, but I know how to deal with him. I'll give his chest a good rubbing wi' goose grease outside, an' make him a basin o' onion gruel to lay warm on his lungs inside. He'll be as right as ninepence in a day or two.'

'I think he really should have a doctor. He is coughing most dreadfully.'

'No, sir, thank you all the same. We can't afford to pay no doctor till we really have to, when somebody's a-dying, like. But it's only the old phlegm on Eddie's chest, same as allus. If it don't move with the onion gruel, I shall have to try linseed an' liquorish. That'll do it—it's a sort o' linseed poultice inside instead of outside, as you might say. You bile the linseed till it's all of a jelly, like, and then put about half-a-hinch o' strong Spanish liquorish in it, an' stir it round well till the liquorish dissolves, an' then eat it as 'ot as ever you can bear it. Eddie don't like the taste o' liquorish, an' it usually makes him sick a while after he's had it—but that's what does good, yer see, sir—it brings up all that old phlegm.'

She was so sure of herself, so calm and capable, that Richard felt his anxiety falling away.

'I'm sure you know best,' he said. 'I'll call in tomorrow, and see how he is.'

He was as good as his word, but he did not like what he found at all. Eddie's eyes were far too bright, his pale cheeks too flushed, his breathing laboured and the coughing worse, if anything. Eddie seemed glad to have him there, but talk was quite impossible, so he sat silently, helping when he could, though there was little he could do. After a particularly bad spell of coughing, Eddie sank back on his pillows and tried to form a smile. His lips moved and Richard read, rather than heard, his request.

'Pray with me.' Not, Richard noticed, 'Pray for me' but 'with me'. Never had he felt so inadequate, so tongue-tied, so unsure of himself. He began to murmur such prayers as he

might have used over a child, and after a minute the sick man
put out a feverish hand and clasped his own. The fervour of
faith seemed to flow from Eddie's work-hardened fingers into
his own, and his voice strengthened as he went on. Eddie
joined in the Lord's Prayer, and said, 'Amen. Thank you,'
with such gratitude that the clergyman's eyes filled.

He left, with the conviction that the patient upstairs was
going to die unless something were done quickly, yet he could
not interfere without permission. He prayed silently to himself, for help and guidance. Within a hundred yards of the
cottage, he came upon Nurse Hardy. He held up his hand to
stop her, and she leapt from her bike to listen. Then they went
back together.

'He's got to have a doctor, quick,' she said. 'Go for Dr
Leathers. I'll stay here.'

'Double pneumonia,' said the doctor. 'We'll do what we
can, but we shan't know which way it's going till the crisis—
usually about the ninth day.'

'Next Friday,' said Nurse, who had worked it out already.
There were still five days to go.

Eddie's condition continued to deteriorate, in spite of all the
doctor's skilled attention. By Wednesday he had slipped into
feverish delirium alternating at rare intervals with periods of
exhausted lucidity. In his delirium he cycled through wind and
storm, loaded carts with heavy sacks till the perspiration
soaked through to the mattress on which he lay, and preached
with all the fervour of his fevered mind the sermons he had
worked so hard at in the past. In his lucid intervals he prayed
and thanked God for the good life he had had. He asked for
Richard Ellis every time he came to himself, if by chance the
young clergyman happened not to be present, but often he
was there. He spent every moment that was possible at Eddie's
bedside, sensing the other man's need of him. He undertook
many of the long night watches, when Eddie's mother and
sisters, worn out with work and anxiety, had to leave him, and
rest. Nurse went twice every day to change the bed-linen

and do what she could to make the patient comfortable. She seemed to have a great calming influence on him, even in delirium, though often it took two of them to keep him from rising in order to 'witness'. Luke Townsend offered his services as 'sitter-up', and came into the bedroom prepared to stop; but his presence seemed to excite the patient. 'Don't you come near me, you bible-creeping old humbug,' Eddie said, glaring wildly at him. Luke was cut to the quick, but obeyed Nurse's gentle refusal to let him stay. 'It is often the way,' she explained as she went downstairs with Luke. 'When it comes as near to the end as this, they often turn against the people they have thought most of. Don't take it to heart. He has no idea what he is saying.'

He raved and struggled all through Thursday night, and towards morning seemed better; but when Nurse and doctor met at his bedside in the late afternoon of Friday, they needed only to look at each other to convey a hopeless message.

'Can you stay with him, Nurse?' asked Dr Leathers. 'I think if you can, you should. You can do him no good, but there are others to think about.'

For once in a lifetime of nursing, almost, Nurse seemed to be about to refuse, but changed her mind.

'I must do one or two visits, and go home for a meal and a bath,' she said. 'But I'll be back by nine o'clock, and stay all night if necessary.' She left with the doctor, and paid a quick visit to Cudweed before going on.

Richard Ellis came in to sit with Eddie. About six o'clock he suddenly became calm, slept for a few minutes, and then opened his eyes again quite clear headed.

'I think I'm passing away,' he said. 'Am I?'

Richard could do no more than stretch out his hand to press the thin, fevered one endlessly folding the sheet.

'I'm not afraid, you know. Only sorry I shan't be able to carry on the Lord's work. But He knows best. His will be done.'

After a few minutes he opened his eyes again, and asked to

232

see all his family. They came—his mother, brothers and sisters—and stood around his bed dumb with grief and disbelief. One by one he commended them to Jesus, and then exhorted them to care for his mother—especially his brothers, who now must take on his share of loving as well as their own. They crept away, awed by his calm. Richard still stayed on.

Then Eddie asked for his friends. 'Who? Which?' asked Richard. Eddie named Luke first, then Alice and Gladys. By the time they came to him, Nurse had come back. Alice dissolved in tears, but Gladys, full of calm dignity, joined in the prayers Eddie demanded, and then they left. He slept again.

'It looks as if we shall be the last watchers, tonight,' said Nurse. 'I doubt if he will survive till morning.'

Later on, Eddie regained consciousness once more though very weak, and asked feebly for Miss Taylor.

His 'watchers' were surprised, and wondered if he were wandering in his mind again.

'She teached me when I was a littl'un,' said Eddie, lapsing into the dialect of his babyhood. 'She used to sing with us, and tell us stories. I remember them all, same as if it was only yesterday. Tell her I want her. She'll come.'

She did come, willingly, and Nellie with her. In spite of her self-control, Miss Taylor could not hide her tears. The boy looked at her with loving, respectful eyes. To him, she was Authority in physical form, and she and Nurse together represented the rocks of earthly security he was about to abandon. Nellie stood by the window, as Nurse wiped Eddie's forehead and Miss Taylor sat by the foot of the bed, with Richard on the other side. The time wore on with leaden feet towards dawn.

'Sing to me, Miss Taylor,' he said, opening his eyes at last.

'What shall I sing?'

'Jesus loves me.' It was a hymn they sang in the very babies' class at school. Miss Taylor looked to Nellie for help and support, and began to sing the children's hymn. Eddie listened with a look of infinite content.

233

'Can you sing, "Come over the line, it's only a step, A step between me and Jesus"?' It was a Sankey and Moody hymn that Miss Taylor was not well acquainted with, and she hesitated; but Eddie himself began to sing, and Nellie joined in. The words came back to Miss Taylor, and between them, brokenly, they managed to finish it.

'Open the window,' said Eddie. 'Open it wide.'

Nellie looked at Nurse doubtfully.

'Open it, so I can get out.'

Miss Taylor laid a restraining hand on him. 'You mustn't catch cold again,' she said.

Nurse took a bold decision. 'Please do as he asks,' she said to Nellie, 'wide open as far as you can get it.' Then she went to the head of the bed and sat beside her patient, lifting the frail body till he too was sitting upright. She placed her own comfortable, solid form behind him, to support him, motioning to Richard to help on the other side. Miss Nellie and her sister stood at each side of the opened casement window.

'Sing it again,' he said, and they began; but before they reached the end of the second line, Eddie sat up of his own accord, reached out his arms, and cried, 'I'm coming, Lord, I'm coming!'

In the early dawn Nurse left the bereaved family. She was utterly weary, drained of all vitality, and emotionally worn out. It was now 6.30 am on her second wedding day.

17 Hanging and wiving

They had decided to be married as soon as possible after the legal formalities would permit, but Jack, though stolidly determined on his course, could not help at the same time applying the fatalistic philosophy of most country people. Something might yet go wrong. 'Best be on the safe side' was a motto he had always put into practice. They would keep their secret, as far as the actual wedding was concerned, until 'the papers' were actually in Nurse's hands. She had tried to do a bit of forward planning, all the same, and had asked for the Easter weekend off duty, with the rest of that week as part of her annual leave. She would for the time being have to retain her own council house for her successor, if she and Jack decided she should not go on working. As it was at the moment, she could not give in her notice, so she would have to continue into the coming summer.

Leave for the holiday weekend had been refused, on the grounds that other district nurses in the adjoining villages expected several midwifery calls, and could not cover for her. Reluctantly, she and Jack had decided to put everything forward a week, though this was running the decree absolute pretty close. It was this last bit of uncertainty that had prevented any preparations whatsoever at Cudweed, where Jack would have liked to make some changes before his new wife came to take up residence.

He found himself, therefore, on the morning of his second venture into matrimony, doing his milking at 5 am as usual and afterwards joining Percy Winters in the rest of the yard work as soon as the horsekeeper had finished baiting the two horses that still remained on the farm. It was while they were strawing the bullock yard that he suddenly took the plunge.

'Perce,' he said. 'I'm going to be away for three or four days, from today. You'll manage all right without me, shan't you? Do the milking yourself if you like, an' if not, get Dave Stevens to do it.'

'Goin' for a holiday then?' asked Perce, in the flat, matter-of-fact tones that concealed surprise and incredulity.

'I'm going to get married today,' Jack said.

Perce leaned on his pitchfork and stared. Like everybody else, he had heard rumours, but had never really given them credence. He was too nonplussed with the thoughts that raced through his mind for his slow tongue to utter anything.

'Ah. I'll see to everything then,' was all he could say. Jack was relieved, but he had more to ask.

'Look here, Perce,' he said. 'There's reasons why me and Nurse haven't told nobody before now, and you're the only one as knows. I shall be obliged if you'd keep your mouth shut till I get back.'

Perce nodded. 'Can I tell Else?'

'Yes, but ask her not to say anything to anybody, either.'

'Elsie won't split,' said Perce. 'You know 'ow she feels about gossippin'.'

Jack was more than surprised at his intended bride's appearance in the early morning, obviously weary. She told him hurriedly of Eddie's death, and had a cup of tea with him. Neither of them could really believe that within twelve hours from now they would be man and wife. Their relationship was still more of a deep, satisfying friendship than a middle-aged romance. They discussed the arrangements for the rest of the day as if they were merely planning a trip to market together.

Under the circumstances of Cudweed not having been, as Jack put it, 'spruced up', he suggested that they should go straight on from the registrar's office in town for a few days' touring holiday, stopping when and where they could at night.

'So pack a bag, and I'll pick you up about quarter past eleven,' he said, holding her head between his hands while he dropped a kiss on the end of her nose. Her eyes filled with tears, as she caught his hand and laid her face against it. It was difficult to believe that things could turn out as right as this for anyone, let alone for her.

After she'd gone, Jack put his own things together, and went downstairs to have his breakfast. He was still sitting at the table when Elsie arrived. She was flushed, and red round the eyes. She barely acknowledged his cheery good morning, but set herself to work with fury, banging and clashing crockery in the sink, scattering cats and kittens as she picked up mats from the floor, and attacking every bit of furniture that happened to be in her way as though it were a personal enemy.

'In one of her tantrums today,' Jack told himself, as she sent a cloud of dust from the grate whirling round his head. He stood up and reached for his cap. 'Has Perce told you?' he said.

She sent more ashes flying beneath her stove brush. 'Ah. He said something about it.'

'It won't make any difference to your job, Else,' he said. 'You see, Nurse has got to go on working for quite a while yet, so I hope you'll still look after this place for us. In fact, I'm hoping you'll do a bit of extra this week, and re-arrange things upstairs a bit, do you understand?'

She polished even more furiously.

'I dunno. I shall have to see,' she said primly, with her mouth drawn into a thin horizontal line. Jack looked hard at her, but she wouldn't turn her face towards him again. He was so used to her that he hardly ever looked at her, but it did strike him this morning that she was a very peculiar woman. He wondered what sort of a married life poor old Perce had. Elsie was too tall, too angular, too unyielding in every respect to make a man comfortable with her. 'Like trying to make love to a clothes' post,' he thought, and good humour swept through him and over him as he compared Elsie's thin, tough frame with Nurse's plump, comforting curves. He felt he was a lucky man.

Eddie's death was occupying the village to the exclusion of all else. 'Every man's death diminishes me,' quoted the Professor sadly, agreeing with Richard Ellis that nowhere was the truth of Donne's words so palpably evident as in a close-knit village. It was as though life had gone out of the whole community, and it could only say, like Antony,

> 'My heart is in the coffin there with Caesar,
> And I must pause till it come back to me.'

Richard Ellis asked the Rev. Costello to conduct the funeral service on Monday, because he wanted to identify himself personally with the mourners. Costello agreed, and was therefore preparing to set out when the second post of the day brought him another letter.

Dear vicar
do not be surprized if somebody as was once a churchwarden as got hisself in a mess with a a woman what still as an husband living why should they get married in a register office. There isn't no call for that if he is a widowman as we no and she is a widow as we don't no. will he come to church Easter Day and take sacriment i wonder, i felt that you should no about it in good time.

There was no signature.

Costello stood with the letter in his hand, and faced its disturbing consequences. He sent for Richard, and showed him it.

'It must be from the same person who sent Mrs Evans that other one,' Richard said.

Costello would not be side-tracked. 'Do you know whom it refers to?' he said. 'It can only be Marriatt, can't it? Who is the woman?'

Richard remembered Nurse as she had held Eddie while he died, only three days before.

'I think Nurse Hardy is meant,' he said. 'But you can't seriously take notice of this thing, surely! We have no proof whatsoever that there is any truth in it for one thing. I haven't heard a word about any intended marriage, though the village has been full of talk about a suspected romance.'

'I shall make it my business to find out, if possible,' the Vicar replied. 'If a man who has been a church member from his cradle chooses to marry in a registrar's office, there can only be one reason for it, as the writer of this letter has rightly concluded. I doubt, if Marriatt really has done so, whether he would present himself at the altar rail; but I can take no chances. I shall speak to him after the funeral today.'

'He happens to be away,' said Richard. 'It seems he is taking the first holiday he's ever had, though I believe he is coming back on Wednesday.'

'Indeed? And Nurse Hardy?'

'Well—she is off duty,' agreed the curate reluctantly. He hesitated.

'You know, Sir,' he went on, 'I can't honestly feel that it is such a sin for two good people like Jack Marriatt and Nurse to find happiness together whatever the situation. It would surely be more Christian of us all to wish them well! At their age, it is probably a "complete" marriage—much more likely to stand up to the demands of the marriage service than that of a couple of unthinking youngsters.'

'Those whom God hath joined together, let no man put asunder.'

'But surely, Vicar—no man could put asunder those whom *God* had joined together?'

239

'I will have none of this modern thinking in my parishes! Christ made it quite explicit that such a marriage was adulterous. It therefore breaks the seventh commandment.'

'What, doth no man condemn thee? Neither do I condemn thee. Go, and sin no more,' said the curate under his breath.

'Ellis—on this matter you will obey my instructions without question. Christian marriage is the rock upon which the family, the community, the nation and the church all have their foundations. The church's stand on the marriage of divorced people is unequivocal. If it is true that Marriatt has chosen to re-marry in a registrar's office, that is a sad thing for a good churchman to have done, but it does not concern us. If, however, the reason for such an action is—as the writer of this letter concludes—that the woman he has married has a husband still living, that is a very different matter. I could not allow him to take the body and blood of Christ, who so expressly forbade it; I should refuse to serve him. I forbid you to serve him, either.'

'But we don't *know*,' said Richard. 'We can't take such a serious action without proof.'

'We shall know before Sunday,' said Costello. 'As I said, I intend to make it my business to find out.'

Richard's heart was doubly heavy as he cycled to Eddie's funeral. It was fast being borne in on him that if he were to continue in the church he had to do a great deal of heart-searching. Accepting doctrinal points in the abstract was one thing, but when it came down to people you knew and respected, it was another. His thoughts switched to the growing seriousness of the international situation. Perhaps he should begin to extricate himself from this comfortable little backwater, where a ripple caused by a falling feather seemed like a tidal wave, and begin to find himself a job as an army chaplain. He sighed as the church tower came into view, with the village it protected clinging round it like children to the skirts of their mother.

'Love one another' was just as much a commandment as the

240

seventh law of Moses, he reflected. He wondered what Eddie would have made of it all.

He walked by the side of Harriet Payne as the sad cortège left the south door of the church and wound its way round the east end to the north side of the graveyard. There Whippet had prepared a grave as near to the church as he could manage it, by the side of the path and in the shade of a huge oak tree, self-sown there centuries ago.

Those of the village who were not present were conspicuous by their absence, Richard thought. It was surprising how many people were genuinely mourning the loss of their bright-haired young preacher.

Mrs Watson was at the organ, and Richard was glad of the hearty singing of so many of the chapel people gathered in the beautiful old building. At his mother's request, they had sung Eddie's favourite chapel hymn, remembering how he would quote the words of one particular verse, whenever he was in doubt or distress:

I know not where His islands lift
Their fronded palms in air.
I only know I cannot drift
Beyond His love and care.

Richard felt strangely comforted.

The Vicar left the church after the usual words of condolence to the bereaved family, and went to his car, which he had left in Charlie's yard, so as not to be in the way. He saw with irritation that Mrs Vernon was standing by it, obviously waiting for him. He did not wish to be delayed. He had made up his mind to consult somebody likely to know the truth about Jack Marriatt and Nurse, and had decided that Miss Taylor was the best bet. She was not at the funeral, as school was still in session until the following Wednesday; but he intended to call at the school, and wait till she could give him her attention.

Mrs Vernon was agitated, however, and begged him to

accompany her home for a cup of tea, as she needed badly to consult him.

As soon as the tea was made, she placed before him a letter, on blue, lined paper that he recognized only too well.

Dear mrs Vernon,
I rite to let you no as jack Marriatt and Nurse Hardy as got married on saturday in the registry office because she is a divorced woman with an husband still living why else should they keep it all so secret and underhand, it is not rite for a church man to get married anywhere else only church but it is not him it is her as i think you ought to no about becuase you have had her and her low-lived concert party as she calls it to help you at the mother's union. and she new well enough all the while that she was divorced and you wouldn't have had her if you had new as well. so she is a lying bitch as well as a bad woman and i hope you never have nothing else to do with her.

'This is a really serious matter, Mrs Vernon,' he said. He meant the writing of anonymous letters. She took him to be referring to the contents of the one she had just shown him.

'It is, indeed,' she said, her heavy jowl shaking with indignation and worry. 'I have good cause to be sorry that I ever allowed the Mothers' Union to be involved with that vulgar concert party! I have always tried to educate the taste of the people in the villages I have lived in, but I must say I almost despair of them by now. As you saw for yourself that night, the low kind of entertainment that concert party provides is very popular. If what this letter suggests is true, I have much more cause for regret—though to be truthful, it was all Nellie Taylor's fault and not my doing. I can't help feeling that whoever this anonymous writer is, he or she has hit the nail on the head. Nurse Hardy has been very well respected; but if she has been amongst us, living a lie, all these years, it is a positive disgrace.'

'Now don't distress yourself unnecessarily, especially about the concert party,' he said. 'I own that at first I was much surprised—even shocked. But I considered later that my judgment had been too hasty. These people have a culture of their own, you know, into which people like us cannot ever be wholly assimilated. It would not be good for us, or them, if we could. That is really a minor issue.

'But on the rules of the church, as in the case of divorce, for instance, we have a duty to stand firm at all costs. And here, I think, the backing of a great many village people will be on our side. I, too, have had one of these letters. It must be from the same pen.'

They compared the two letters in silence, and noted that the content was concerned very largely with the same item of news. The Vicar suddenly clicked his tongue. She looked inquiringly.

'I had one of these communications some time ago,' he said. 'It was on the subject of another matter, at least, on the surface. But it did contain an innuendo about another person—or persons—in one of my parishes. It has just come to me that it was probably pointing to Marriatt and Nurse Hardy. If whoever the writer is had good evidence as long ago as that, I'm afraid we must fear the worst.' He was genuinely distressed.

He rose, and stood looking out of the window. The village lay stretched before him. To the left he could see the church, where Whippet was by this time filling in the earth on Eddie's coffin; the school, with a line of children playing 'Blacktop' against the wooden fence; the shop, where a group of women, all still in their black, were gathered round the door.

In front of him stretched the lane to Stavesacre; and to his right, after passing several houses and cottages, the road went out of sight and round a bend that led it to a junction with the cart road up to Cudweed. Why could it not all be as idyllic as it looked?

'One comes to accept a certain amount of laxity on the question of sexual behaviour from people who live in country villages, you know,' he said. 'For centuries they have been practically cut off from the outside world, and many of them live very narrow lives still, very close to nature. But one does have a right to expect in these enlightened days that the professional people among them—the doctor, the nurse, the school teacher—should set them examples to follow. Marriatt is a countryman, but he is much respected; until recently he has been a good churchman. I believe we have the right to expect such as he to obey the precepts of the Church. I can only feel it my duty to confront him on his return with the matter contained in these—er—letters. I should be obliged if you could be there with me as a witness. If, as I hope, we find no truth at all in it, I shall apologize, and ask him whether or not he wishes me to take these letters to the police. If we should find the accusations warranted, then it will be my duty to warn him that he cannot expect to be given the Holy Sacrament on Easter Day or at any other time. He will, I understand, be home on Wednesday. I shall be there at approximately 3 pm.' He left.

Meanwhile, the sinners concerned had been securely tied together as far as civil law goes by a cheerful, matter-of-fact registrar, and had wandered off in a dreamlike state towards the nearest coast. A little market town offered them homely accommodation and a plain but well cooked evening meal. The new Mrs Marriatt had gone up for a bath while Jack lit his favourite pipe and wandered out along the street. He mused upon the workings of fate that had brought him there. He was barely able to believe it.

When his pipe was nearly finished, he went back to the hotel and straight upstairs. He was wryly amused to realize how much courage it needed. He opened the bedroom door, pipe still in his mouth.

She was fast asleep already and gently snoring. He remembered with contrition that she had been up all night at Eddie's bedside, and had had no chance to rest. He undressed, moving as quietly as a mouse, treading the ancient creaking floorboards with surprising lightness for so large a man. Then he crept into bed beside her, piled up the pillows behind him, and smoked his pipe out. As he put out the light, he reflected that he was perhaps, if not the happiest, the most contented man alive. It occurred to him as he drifted towards sleep that God must be very much cheered up by an occasional acknowledgment that man is satisfied with his lot. Prayer and praise in a nutshell.

They reached home on Wednesday afternoon. The kitchen was swept and garnished, and the fire laid in the grate. Jack put a match to it, and filled the kettle. A letter stood against the tea-caddy on the high mantelpiece, addressed to him.

Dear mr. Marriatt (he read)

I have left things as good as i can for you when you come home but i must tell you as i shall not be able to do for you no longer becuase i have not enjoy good health myself lately and i have served you well for a long while ever since your wife passed away poor thing what would she have said i wonder.

But you will not need me no more now you have another woman in the house so i give you notice as i shall not come up no more

and oblige
Mrs P. Winters.

He stood staring as if petrified at the letter, and look of utter bewilderment and disbelief on his face. He was about to show it to his wife when the Vicar's car drew up to the door. Being already on his feet, Jack opened the door as the clergyman climbed down from The Fire Engine, and Mrs Vernon approached on foot. They were both asked in, while Jack made apologies for the lack of warmth, so far, in the house.

The visitors looked around and about and saw what they had come to see. Jack followed their gaze, and read their expressions.

'I believe you both know my wife,' he said. 'You are our first visitors. As soon as the kettle boils, we'll all have a cup of tea to celebrate.'

They murmured a polite refusal intertwined with

lukewarm congratulations. Then the vicar took the bull by the horns.

'Mrs Vernon and I have both received anonymous letters, a day or two after you left,' he said. 'I should like you to read them.' He spread them out before Jack, and watched as the pleasant, open expression of the farmer turn to one of distress, and then of anger. Jack's first thought was that 'Nurse' should not read them, but he was too late. She stretched out her hand.

'It's somebody a bit queer in the head,' she said. 'This can't be the work of any normal person. I'm sure it's a woman. Such malice can only be inspired by jealousy. Why don't we just burn the wretched things, and think no more about them? Look—Jack and I are married now. It doesn't matter what people say, does it? If we knew who was writing the letters, it would be different. Whoever she is, she needs help.'

'I'm afraid I do know who it could be,' Jack said slowly, in a troubled voice. He laid down Elsie's 'notice' by the side of the other two, for the Vicar and Mrs Vernon to read.

'It appears to me that there can't be much doubt,' he concluded. The Vicar reluctantly agreed.

'It is on the same paper, in the same hand, in the same style, and with the same spelling mistakes—"becuase" for instance.'

'It *can't* be,' expostulated Mrs Vernon. 'Elsie Winters is simply the last person who would do such a thing! As she is forever saying, she "doesn't talk scandal".'

'I'm afraid that hasn't prevented her from writing it,' said the Vicar. 'And of course, she would be in a good position to know what she had observed personally.'

'I don't know what you mean by that,' said Jack, face and voice hard. 'It certainly does make a lot of sense, if Elsie has been spying—perhaps even listening under the window. But there's been nothing going on here that she could observe, so I'll tell you that for nothing! Poor old Perce. I shall be sorry to lose him, but they'll have to go.' His face was grim. He turned to the Vicar, fair and square. 'This bit about taking the sacrament—what does she mean by that?'

'She is quite right about it, of course, if your wife has a husband living.' Mrs Vernon nodded agreement.

'Of course she's got a husband living! I'm standing here in front of you! If you mean that bloody fellow who was her husband once, why don't you say so? But what's that got to do with it? I ain't got no other wife now. She died—my first wife—before either of you came here.'

'I'm afraid that makes no difference. If your wife has a divorced partner still living, the church can only regard your civil marriage as adulterous. In the light of that, I'm afraid I shall have to refuse you the Sacrament. I must obey the rules laid down by the bishop.'

Jack sat down heavily. 'There's Marriatts in the church registers back as far as the fourteen hundreds,' he said. 'And you've only got to look at the gravestones to see the church-wardens as lay there, all Marriatts, back to the eighteenth century. I was christened in that church, confirmed there, and married there. I buried my first wife there, and served it as long as I could myself, as a churchwarden. And now the church is turning me out, is it? Well, let it! I'm the last o' the Marriatts, anyway. There's no son to follow me, here at Cudweed or up there in the graveyard. If I ever set foot in that church again o' my own free will, it will be because some bloody parson has invited me, and my wife with me.'

'Jack! Jack!' from his wife. 'Don't lose your temper. It isn't worth it.'

Jack looked squarely at the clergyman. 'I didn't know,' he said. 'Perhaps that's because I'm such a simpleton—but I didn't know. If it wasn't happening to me, I shouldn't believe it! I should have said that the God I believed in would have wanted people who'd had a lot o' trouble to help themselves when they could, and wouldn't want to punish 'em just for being happy again. But I'll tell you one thing, straight to your face. If I had known, it wouldn't have made a bloody scrap of difference. So you needn't bother your head about us any

247

more. We'll find our own way to heaven from now on, without your help.'

There was bitter silence all round, except for the nervous clucking of Mrs Vernon's throat.

Jack picked up the letters. 'You've been pretty keen on making my business your own,' he said. 'Perhaps you'd better be the one to deal with the other black sheep among your flock. I daresay you'll find Elsie at home if you go now.'

Mrs Marriatt suddenly became 'Nurse' again. She broke in before the Vicar had time to answer.

'I suggest you go alone,' she said, looking pointedly at Mrs Vernon. 'I think you'll have to handle it all very gently as well. I wouldn't myself like to take the consequences. If it is Elsie Winters—and there can't be much doubt—she must be out of her mind—ill, not just wicked. I've seen it so many times before! A woman at a difficult age, bottling up grievances till they get out of hand. Every woman at that age feels that something is being taken away from her, I believe. When her children have gone, she feels unwanted, and that nobody needs her. In Elsie's case, it was Jack that needed her. Then there's this not "talking scandal" business. Most village scandal boils down to sex. Talking about it is a sort of substitute for a lot of women, especially in the years of the change. Elsie has deliberately deprived herself of gossiping and it has just burst out in another way. I think she should just be let alone till she gets used to the idea of me being here. It's probably only just a passing phase, and the only person who could really help her is a doctor.'

The Vicar was not to be dissuaded from seeing her, in case she should make more mischief.

'She is a member of my church,' he said. 'I think she will take reproof from me. In fact, she probably anticipates just such a visit, sooner or later.'

'Psychological nonsense,' was the Vicar's comment to himself as he walked the short distance to the Winters' cottage.

When confronted with the charge, Elsie indignantly denied

all, with well-simulated injured innocence. The Vicar pressed home with his evidence. He suggested that she should write a few lines at his dictation. She became flustered, but he pushed paper and pencil before her.

'Take it as a test to prove your innocence, not your guilt,' he said. 'Write "I want to let you know because———" ' he got no further. She began to cry, and then to shriek, and at last to swear, using a vocabulary from the farmyard that was new in the Vicar's experience. Her vituperation poured out, mainly on the head of Jack and his wife, until she had exhausted herself, and sank sobbing with her head on the old wooden table.

The Vicar remembered Nurse's warning then, and spoke gently and kindly, though firmly.

'Now, Mrs Winters—no one who knows the truth about these letters will ever say a word, I can promise you that. Not even your husband need ever know; but I must ask in return for a promise that you will never write another. You could have done a great deal of harm—indeed, you have probably done so already. Will you promise?'

She nodded, and he left. He would have liked to find words of comfort and help for her, but he could not unbend. He would never have any true rapport with such people. He suddenly realized how much he needed Richard Ellis to complement him, and to make up for his own shortcomings in that respect.

It was late next afternoon that Percy, going home for his tea, discovered that Elsie was missing, and went back to consult Jack.

At eight o'clock, Jack went for the police, and roused some other men to search for her. It was the next morning before they found her, hanging from a beam by her own new clothes-line, in a disused barn behind the wood on the very outskirts of the Priory Estate.

'It 'ad to be,' said Sammy to Reg Pettigrew. 'It 'ad to be. Every now and then that old tree has to take another victim, like, even if they don't do it just there.'

'It 'ad to be,' said George Willis to Charlie. 'There's some

249

things as can't be stopped no 'ow. If it's writ down in the Lamb's book o' life, it 'as to be, though you can wriggle about trying to get out of it like a bloody worm on a pin, till your guts is all a-'anging on one thread. When folks mean to do it, they will, choose 'ow. You can set up o' nights an' watch 'em, but if they've a mind to do it, they'll find a way. There ain't no way o' stoppin' 'em.'

'It 'ad to be,' said Perce to Jack. 'After all, she were a Tibbs afore I married her, wa'n't she? 'Angin's in her blood, as you might say. Only I'd sort of forgot, bein' married to her for so long, till I come in an' found out she were missing. I knowed then as we should find her 'ung. Poor old Else.'

With a tragic death, a controversial marriage, and a suicide in their very midst, it was hardly surprising that the village failed to take much notice of the disappearance of Austria, the resignation of the Foreign Secretary, or the growling rumbling of Winston Churchill. Nevertheless ARP became letters with which they were vaguely familiar, and Charlie became the first ARP warden, with a post set up in 'the room' at The Star, in which, from time to time, he demonstrated to the few who would bother to listen how to put on a gas mask.

When the Sudetenland was grabbed by Germany, it was high summertime again. Weary with long days of work in the sunshine, men and women alike dropped to sleep without concern for the happenings so far away in a country whose name they couldn't even pronounce. It was a good harvest, and Luke Townsend, walking his farm to see which of the fields of wheat and oats was ready next for cutting, looked at the silver and gold bowl in which the village lay, and rejoiced.

> The valleys stand so thick with corn
> That even they are singing.

For once the words rang true.

There were a few, like Charlie, who watched the newspapers with worried expressions and listened with apprehension to the next nine o'clock news.

'Gas masks! Whatever next!' snorted Aunt Mabel. 'If you ask me, that Anthony Eden an' that there Winston Churchill want gas masks hangin' on their backsides! They won't let well alone. Keep stirring Hitler up like a boy poking a stick in a hornets' nest. It's none of our business what goes on in Checkowhateveritis and them outlandish parts. Chamberlain would soon settle it, if such as Churchill'd keep their mouths shut.

' 'Im and his bloody umbrella,' retorted Uncle Bert. 'I wouldn't give you a shilling for a scuttleful o' men like 'im! If Mr Attlee were Prime Minister, we shouldn't have no reason to quarrel wi' this 'Itler. They're both on 'em Socialists—'Itler were a working man hisself once. It just shows what ordinary yuman beings like 'im can do, if the upper classes 'll give 'em a proper chance. Attlee wouldn't have no truck with all this war talk. It's all vested interest, that's what it is, vested interest.' (He loved using phrases that Aunt Mabel didn't know the meaning of.)

'Vested interest my arse,' said Aunt Mabel vulgarly. 'Vested 'umbug, that's what your darling Clementine Attlee is. Vested 'umbug.'

'Can you really believe such hignorance?' Uncle Bert asked May, as if Aunt Mabel were a deaf mute or an idiot child over whose head they could talk with impunity.

'They're at it again,' said May cheerfully to a shop full of customers.

'Our Sid says they're only doing what's right, making us have gas masks and sich,' Mrs Bluett confided in her stentorian tones. 'Sid were in the war, and he seed a lot o' men what had been gassed wi' that 'orrible phosdyke gas. Whole bastillions o' men were catched in it, an' killed. Turned green, they did, Sid said.'

' 'Ang the old war! I don't 'old with it,' said Harriet, in massive understatement, as Richard Ellis called to bid her farewell.

The corn harvest had almost all been gathered in by the time the Prime Minister began his diplomatic shuttle between London and Germany. Sun-soaked and weary, they turned on their wireless sets to hear his broadcast to the nation: 'How horrible, fantastic, incredible it is that we should be digging trenches and trying on gas masks here because of a quarrel in a faraway country between people of whom we know nothing . . .'

That was it. They agreed with him. He was still trying to keep the peace. Many allowed his voice to lull them into a drowse, long before he had finished his dire warnings. It had been a long day, and it would so soon be morning again.

They were glad when they heard his voice again from the airfield at Heston, bringing them 'peace in our time'. Even Uncle Bert spoke well of him. Everybody relaxed, as work and tension together began to ease off a little.

'O peaceful England, while I my watch am keeping,' hummed the Professor, watching the sunset from his back door, and abandoning the glories of the past for a moment in favour of the pleasures of the present. The end of September was golden indeed.

Stubble once more gleamed ash-blonde in the sunshine, flecked here and there with shadows of stook and bale. The chestnuts up at Cudweed wore golden tips on their long green fingers, and below them the ground was chequered white and green where the spiky casings split open, throwing out the polished brown nuts and revealing the startling white beds in which they had been formed. Pellmell's elms turned fairy-gold, and the hanging tree's silver-white leaves were darkened again with clumsy bunches of keys.

The air was warm, enriched with smells. Every spot had its own faint, persistent, individual scent, so that a blind man could have found his way by following his nose. Beer and furniture polish in The Star, tobacco and cobbler's wax in Don's shop; cheese and pepper in May's tiny post office, soap and disinfectant in the Jeffs's kitchen-cum-bathroom. Yeast and woodsmoke in Harriet's living-room, dogs, cats, and cold tea at Pellmell; perfume in the bedrooms at Stavesacre, and the healthy tang of well-rotted manure in the farmyard; varnished wood in the chapel, old stone, age and brass polish in the church; and everywhere the scent of sun-soaked straw and thatch.

Between two and four o'clock on the first Saturday of October, time stood still. Not just time by the clock on every mantelpiece, or the church clock, still ten minutes slow—but Time. Time that looped together little Tom, drowned in his mother's best October ale, with Eddie, now lying three feet above him under the churchyard oak. Time, that bound Monty Price in his room at The Priory with the virile monk whose restless spirit still 'fetched' The Family home. Time that belittled quarrels, and reminded the young duke in Rhodesia of his heritage of English blood. Time that allowed the Professor to wander in Periclean Athens, and Charlie to put on the hempen cravat with Claude Duval. Time that heals all wounds, and blankets all differences—it is all one now to Gabriel John, and the old duke, and dear old Grandad Woodward.

Just for a breathing space, Time stood still while the village lay like a heap of pebbles in the bottom of a silver-gilt bowl; then the endless chain began once more to move, folding the present into the past, and reaching out into the unknowable, limitless future.

253